D0919259

Set Theory and Logic

ADIWES INTERNATIONAL SERIES

This book is in the
ADDISON-WESLEY SERIES IN LOGIC
Hartley Rogers, Jr., Consulting Editor

Set Theory and Logic

BY ABRAHAM A. FRAENKEL

Late Professor Emeritus
The Hebrew University of Jerusalem

ADDISON-WESLEY PUBLISHING COMPANY

Reading, Massachusetts · Palo Alto · London · Don Mills, Ontario

Copyright © *1966*

ADDISON-WESLEY PUBLISHING COMPANY, INC.

Printed in the United States of America

All rights reserved. This book, or parts thereof,
may not be reproduced in any form without
written permission of the publisher.

Library of Congress Catalog Card No. 66–15524

This is the only authorized English translation of the original German
edition *Mengenlehre und Logik*, published by Duncker and Humblot,
Berlin-München.

QA
248
.F765

Preface

This booklet is not (in the first place) an exposition of set theory but rather a treatment of the logical problems which arise at critical turning points in the development of set theory. For this purpose it is indispensable to outline the fundamental concepts and propositions referring to abstract sets. This program is essentially carried out in Sections 1 through 5; the last two sections are intended to round off the mathematical theory, particularly with respect to ordered and well-ordered sets.

No familiarity with mathematical or logical techniques is presupposed, and the use of symbolic logic has been avoided. Whenever mathematical technique is developed in the book, the reader is in most cases warned by the use of small print. The book, then, is intended for college freshmen in mathematics and logic and for self-instruction, but above all for students of philosophy looking for an easy introduction into the problem of infinity.

Essentially the booklet is a translation of my book *Mengenlehre und Logik* published in 1959 by Duncker and Humblot as Volume II in the series *Erfahrung und Denken*. However, I have adapted the text to the needs of the English-reading public, expecially of American college students, and have expanded the treatment of a few subjects. The discoveries made in 1963 by Paul J. Cohen regarding the Axiom of Choice and the Continuum Problem have been included.

I wish to express my gratitude to the Addison-Wesley Publishing Company for having encouraged me to translate the book into English.

Jerusalem, Israel   A. A. F.
August 1965

v

Contents

Section 1.   Introduction   1

Section 2.   Equivalence and Cardinal Number   4

Section 3.   Infinite Denumerable and Nondenumerable Sets. Transfi-
              nite Cardinals   12

Section 4.   Logical Problems of Finiteness and Infinity. The Axiom of
              Choice   26

Section 5.   Transfinite Cardinals. Paradoxes of Set Theory and
              Attempts at their Elimination   41

Section 6.   Operations with Cardinals   57

Section 7.   Order, Order Types, Ordinal Numbers. The Problem
              of Well-Ordering   67

Conclusion.   The Significance of Set Theory for Mathematics and
              Logic   88

Bibliography   93

Author Index   99

Subject Index   101

List of Symbols 102

Section 1. Introduction

As a rule, in 19th century mathematics, infinity appears only in its "potential" form. This is the form on the basis of which A. L. Cauchy and his successors laid the rigorous foundations of the calculus in the first half of the century. In the second half of the century, K. Weierstrass, G. Cantor, H. Méray, and others used this form to develop arithmetical theories of irrational numbers. They then used these theories to develop the theory of functions.[1] Potential infinity can be illustrated by a very simple example: the expression $\lim_{n \to \infty} (1 / n) = 0$ [read: the limit of $1 / n$, as n tends to infinity, is zero (or infinitely small)] is nothing more than an abbreviation of the statement "the quotient $1 / n$ can be made to approach 0 with *any desired* accuracy if the positive integer n is chosen *sufficiently large*." (The required magnitude of increasing n, then, depends on the desired accuracy of the approximation of 0 by $1 / n$.) There is no question of "infinitely great" or "infinitely small" in this statement, and the symbol ∞ serves only as a concise notation.

It is this situation to which Gauss referred when he wrote in his famous letter to Schumacher in 1831: "In mathematics infinite magnitude may never be used as something final; infinity is only a *façon de parler*, meaning a limit which certain proportions may approach as closely as desired when others are permitted to increase indefinitely." The powerful authority of Gauss among mathematicians and scientists contributed to his remark being followed in an unrestricted sense, and consequently led to the sup-

---

[1] True, Newton, in his *Principia*, had already developed calculus in a rigorous way, faithful to the methods of Greek geometry, and in the fifth book of Euclid's *Elements* the theory of irrational numbers is formulated in such an impeccable way that it remained unequalled up to the 1860's. Yet during the 18th century mathematicians used a vague notion of infinity to derive their far-reaching discoveries in calculus, including infinite series, and silenced their own scruples with d'Alembert's maxim: *Allez en avant et la foi vous viendra* (go on, the confidence in your results will follow). Euclid's—or Eudoxos'— formulation of the theory of real numbers remained forgotten, and at the beginning of the 19th century even such giants of science as Gauss and Cauchy were satisfied with intuitive concepts deriving from geometry, and did not become conscious of the need for an arithmetical foundation of real numbers.

1

pression, over a period of two decades, of the ideas which are the subject matter of this booklet.

On the other hand, the problem of infinity as an *"actual"* absolute magnitude was raised at an early stage of Catholic theology and philosophy, in particular by Augustinus and by Thomas Aquinas and his school. Furthermore, beginning with Aristotle, many great philosophers, such as Lucretius, Hasdai Crescas, Grégoire de Rimini, and, later, Descartes, Spinoza, Leibniz, Locke, Kant, etc. discussed actual infinity. Some were inclined to accept it and others insisted on rejecting it.[2] An important step forward was taken about the middle of the 19th century by the Bohemian clergyman Bernard Bolzano, who may be considered the greatest logician between Leibniz and the development of symbolic and mathematical logic.[3] In his book written in 1847 and published posthumously in 1850, Bolzano clearly describes the peculiar and "paradoxical" properties of actual infinity, in particular the equivalence of an infinite set to a proper part of itself (see p.27). However, these properties were not used by Bolzano to base infinity on a conceptual foundation which would lead to the systematic exploration of the nature of infinity, but were rather listed as a catalogue of quasi-regrettable paradoxes, thus serving a sterile purpose.[4] The term *Menge* (set) seems to appear for the first time in Bolzano's book.

Despite the tentative endeavors of other mathematicians of the 1870's and 1880's (for instance, H. Hankel, A. Harnack, and P. du Bois Reymond), it was really Georg Cantor,[5] the creator of *Mengenlehre* (set theory), who between 1873 and 1897 carefully laid the foundations of the theory of actual infinity, introduced it systematically into mathematics (and philosophy), and developed around it a new branch of mathematics, the theory of sets. Since the turn of the 19th century, set theory has infiltrated into and largely transformed most branches of mathematics.

---

[2] For details and literature we refer to several papers by Cantor published in 1885–1890, which are reprinted in Cantor (1932), pp.370–439. Cf. Gutberlet (1886).

For all literature references see the Bibliography at the end of this booklet. The references are given by the name of the author and the year of publication.

[3] His main book on logic is *Wissenschaftslehre*, first published in 1837, which appeared in several editions. Cf. Scholz (1931, pp. 44ff.) and Bar-Hillel (1952).

[4] In the 1920's it was discovered that the editor of the posthumous book had on his own account inserted some so-called corrections in Bolzano's manuscript. Hence it has become doubtful whether Bolzano himself was responsible for the shortcomings of the book.

[5] Cf. Cantor (1932) and the biography in Fraenkel (1930).

However, Cantor did not set out with the aim of establishing a theory of infinitely great magnitudes. In 1870 he started from concrete mathematical problems in the theory of functions of a real variable, problems which involve distinguishing finitely or infinitely many "exceptional" points, for instance, points of discontinuity. Slowly, overcoming his own reluctance and the obstinate antagonism of most contemporary mathematicians, he moved forward towards the development of general concepts of a revolutionary nature. The following passage, which opens the fifth paper (1883) of his pioneer work *On infinite linear aggregates of points* (1879–1884), is characteristic of his gradual progress.[6]

"The description of my investigations in the theory of aggregates has reached a stage where their continuation has become dependent on a generalization of the concept of real positive integer beyond the present limits; a generalization which takes a direction into which, as far as I know, nobody has yet looked.

I depend on this generalization of the number concept to such an extent that without it I could not freely take even small steps forward in the theory of sets; I hope that this situation justifies or, if necessary, excuses the introduction of seemingly strange ideas into my arguments. In fact the purpose is to generalize or to extend the series of real integers beyond infinity. Daring as this might appear, I express not only the hope but also the firm conviction that in due course this generalization will be acknowledged as a quite simple, appropriate, and natural step. Still I am well aware that by adopting such a procedure I am putting myself in opposition to widespread views regarding infinity in mathematics and to current opinions on the nature of number."

In the present booklet we intend neither to analyze the development of the concept of infinity and of set theory by Cantor nor to give a systematic exposition of the theory of sets as a branch of mathematics. Our aim is rather to develop, in an elementary way, those principal ideas of *abstract set theory*[7] which are closely connected with *logical* problems and methods, and to elaborate on the nature of those connections. Fortunately for those readers who are not familiar with modern mathematics or logic, our aim can be reached, to a large extent, without the use of symbolic logic or much mathematical technique.

---

[6] See Cantor (1932), p. 165.
[7] We do not include the specialization and application of set theory to the theory of sets of points.

Section 2. Equivalence and Cardinal Number

From Section 4 on we shall closely analyze and restrict the concept of *set*. At present, however, we take a somewhat pragmatic attitude; that is to say, we may be satisfied with accepting the notion of a totality (class, set) as intuitively clear or as taken from philosophy, or we may rely upon Cantor's so-called "definition":

"Unter einer 'Menge' verstehen wir jede Zusammenfassung M von bestimmten wohlunterschiedenen Objekten m unserer Anschauung oder unseres Denkens (welche die Elemente von M genannt werden) zu einem Ganzen."[1]

We shall also say that the set *contains* its elements, or that the elements *belong* to the set.

While the term "collection into a whole" hardly contributes much to clarifying the concept of "set," the terms "definite" and "distinct" have well-defined meanings. The former means that, given a set S, it should be possible to decide (at least in principle) for any object whether it belongs to S or not, even if we cannot actually ascertain which of the two is the case. "Distinct" means that all elements of the same set are different, i.e., that a certain object is either contained or not contained in a given set, but is not contained "repeatedly."

For the time being we shall content ourselves with distinguishing between *finite* and *infinite* sets in the obvious sense that a set S is finite if there is a positive integer n such that S contains exactly n, and not more, different elements; otherwise S is infinite. Furthermore, for reasons which we shall soon see, and which had been recognized even before the creation of set theory, by the inventors of mathematical logic (curiously enough,

---

[1] "A *set* is a collection into a whole of definite, distinct objects of our intuition or our thought. The objects are called the *elements* (or *members*) of the set." This is Cantor's definition of 1895 [see Cantor (1932), p.282]. A similar definition had been proposed by Cantor in 1882 and 1883 (*ibidem*, p. 150 and p. 204).

not by Cantor), it is advisable to introduce also an improper set that contains no members at all. It is called the *null set,* or *empty set,* and is denoted by ∅.

We start with

DEFINITION I. If S and T are sets and if every element of S also belongs to T, then S is called a *subset* of T. In particular, S is a *proper subset* of T if T contains at least one element which does not belong to S. One writes $S \subseteq T$ (S is a subset of T) or $S \subset T$ (S is a proper subset of T). (A set "contains" its elements but "includes" its subsets.)

The sets S and T are called *equal* ($S = T$) if each is a subset of the other, i.e., if they contain the same elements. Otherwise they are called *different* ($S \neq T$).

The relation of equality defined here is not an *identity* in the sense of Leibniz (*identitas indiscernibilium,* that is to say, objects that cannot be distinguished from one another are identical) any more than the relation $2 = 6/3$ expresses identity. Hence the definition does not necessarily imply that whenever $S = T$, S and T are themselves elements of exactly the same sets. The relation " = " denotes only equality of *extent,* or *extensionality.* For instance, the set of the even prime numbers equals the set whose only element is 2.

A more impressive example, which, however, is not of a purely logical character, is the following. Early in the 19th century it was discovered, to the surprise of the mathematical world, that not all algebraic equations can be solved "algebraically" (i.e., by means of the four elementary operations and by root extraction), but in general only the equations of degree 1, 2, 3 and 4. In other words, the set D of the degrees of generally solvable equations equals the set F whose elements are the integers 1, 2, 3, 4. However, the statement "it was unknown in the 18th century whether the set D equals the set F" (i.e., whether, for instance, the general equation of degree 5 is solvable or unsolvable) is true. Nevertheless, if in this statement D is replaced by the equal set F, one obtains an absurdity.

According to Definition I, a set is completely determined (in the sense of its being distinguished from other sets) by the totality of its elements. Therefore the set whose elements are just $a, b, c, d, \cdots$ can and will be denoted by

$$\{a, b, c, d, \cdots \}.$$

The order of the elements within the braces { } is arbitrary; for instance, $\{1, 2, 3\} = \{3, 2, 1\}$. In particular, it follows that there exists a unique null set $\emptyset$. If S is infinite then the dots ($\cdots$) are inevitable, and in each particular case it is assumed that their meaning is obvious; e.g., the set of all positive integers is denoted by $\{1, 2, 3, \cdots\}$, the set of all even ones by $\{2, 4, 6, \cdots\}$. Also, the use of dots is convenient for finite sets which contain "many" elements.

Examples of finite sets with any desired number of elements, say n, can easily be given, e.g.,

$$\{1, 2, 3, \cdots, n\}, \qquad \text{or} \qquad \{0, 1, 2, \cdots, n - 1\}.$$

A simple example of an infinite set is the set of all positive integers. Another seemingly simple or intuitively obvious instance is the *continuum*—for example the set of all (mathematical) points situated on a segment on a circle or on an infinite straight line.

It is not accidental that we are dependent on *mathematical* objects for infinite sets. In fact, according to the concepts of modern physics and astronomy, and contrary to 19th-century science, infinite sets seem not to exist in nature.

The *union* (sum) and the *intersection* (inner product) of two sets S_1, S_2 are defined, respectively, as the set that contains *all elements of S_1 or S_2 (or both)* and the set that contains all elements which belong *both to S_1 and to S_2*. Union thus corresponds to the logical operation of (non-exclusive) "or" (disjunction; *vel* in Latin), intersection to the operation of "and" (conjunction). To guarantee the existence of the intersection in every case, even when S_1 and S_2 are *disjoint* (with no common elements), we must admit the null set.

The operations of union and intersection can be extended easily from two sets to finitely many sets, to an infinite *sequence* $(S_1, S_2, \cdots, S_k, \cdots)$ of sets,[2] and even to any set of sets. For the reader's convenience we shall occasionally use the symbol $+$ (instead of $\cup$, which is more customary nowadays) in forming a union. Both operations are *commutative* and *associative*, and they are connected by two *distributive* laws.

---

[2] In a sequence the order of the elements is important, in contrast to the case of sets, where the order is irrelevant; S_k above is the kth element of the sequence. As is customary, we use parentheses, ( ), to denote sequences.

Most readers will be familiar with the terms "commutative," "associative," and "distributive" from ordinary arithmetic, where we have

$$a + b = b + a, \quad a \cdot b = b \cdot a \text{ (commutative laws)},$$
$$a + (b + c) = (a + b) + c, \quad a \cdot (b \cdot c) = (a \cdot b) \cdot c \text{ (associative laws)},$$
$$a \cdot (b + c) = (a \cdot b) + (a \cdot c) \text{ (distributive law)}.$$

While the commutative and associative laws are formally the same for the operations of union and intersection and also apply to infinitely many terms, as the reader can easily prove, their intrinsic meaning is different. This is mainly due to the fact that in arithmetic, multiplication is based on addition (repeated addition of the same term; cf. Section 6), while the operations of union and intersection are independent and even "dual." We shall show this by explicitly stating and proving the distributive laws. To avoid confusion with arithmetic we shall use the customary symbols, $\cup$ for union and $\cap$ for intersection. Then the distributive laws, for sets a, b, c, are as follows:

$$a \cap (b \cup c) = (a \cap b) \cup (a \cap c), \quad a \cup (b \cap c) = (a \cup b) \cap (a \cup c).$$

The proof is easy, if we remember that the equality of two sets means that they contain the same elements. As far as the first equality is concerned, any element of $a \cap (b \cup c)$ belongs to both a and $b \cup c$, hence to a and to b or c, hence to a and b or to a and c, hence to $(a \cap b) \cup (a \cap c)$. The transition from the right to set to $a \cap (b \cup c)$ is equally simple. As far as the second equality is concerned, any element of $a \cup (b \cap c)$ belongs to a or to both b and c, hence to a or b and to a or c, hence to $(a \cup b) \cap (a \cup c)$. Again, the transition from the right to the left is just as easy.

It is remarkable that the two distributive laws are *dual* to each other, i.e., each results from the other when $\cup$ is replaced everywhere by $\cap$ and $\cap$ by $\cup$. The same holds for the commutative and associative laws.

Abstract systems constructed on the operations of union and intersection (or, in logical language, on disjunction and conjunction) are called *Boolean algebras* after G. Boole, who, together with A. de Morgan, invented these algebras and the corresponding logical calculus. Boolean algebras play an important part in pure and applied mathematics as well as in (symbolic) logic.

The concepts of correspondence and *mapping* are fundamental in what we shall develop below. If to each element s of the set S there corresponds a single element t of a set T, we speak of a single-valued (unique) correspondence. However, the same t may correspond to different s, as is the case for the father-child relationship (t is the father of s). While this kind of correspondence is fundamental for the theory of functions ("univalent function"), in what follows we shall be much more concerned with an additional specialization, namely, *one-to-one* (biunique) *correspondences*, whereby a single t of T corresponds to each s of S, and, moreover, a single s corresponds to each t; i.e., the members of S can be paired off with those of T. In other words, the single-valued correspondence is then also uniquely *invertible*.

The correspondence of husbands to wives is biunique in a monogamic society but only unique in a polygamic one.

A one-to-one correspondence of the members of T to those of S is also called a *mapping of T onto S*, or *between S and T*. The latter expression is justified by the symmetry between S and T, which is based on the biuniqueness of the correspondence. We now introduce

DEFINITION II. *S is called* equivalent *to T, in symbols, $S \sim T$, if there exists a mapping of the set T onto the set S.*

Obviously, any set is equivalent to itself ($S \sim S$); moreover, $S \sim T$ implies $T \sim S$, in view of the symmetry of the mapping. From the relations $S \sim T$ and $T \sim U$ there follows $S \sim U$, in view of the existence of simultaneous mappings of S onto T and of T onto U. One expresses these three properties of $\sim$ by saying that the relation of equivalence is *reflexive, symmetrical,* and *transitive.* Clearly the relation of equality (Definition I) has the same three properties.

Because of symmetry, $S \sim T$ may be also expressed by "S and T are equivalent."

If S contains more than one member, then there exist several mappings between S and any equivalent set, and infinitely many mappings if S is an infinite set.

"x is a prime number" is a *property* (of integers x) or, in more general terminology, a one-place predicate. "$x \sim y$" and "x is smaller than y" are two-place predicates or, for brevity, (binary) *relations.* This distinction does not usually show in the grammatical structure of correspondent sentences and was therefore overlooked by logicians from Aristotle to the second half of the 19th century. Only with the development of symbolic logic, and in particular through the work of Bertrand Russell, did mathematicians and logicians perceive the fundamental difference between properties and (binary, ternary, $\cdots$, n-ary) relations. Ternary relations, for instance, are such expressions as "$x+y=z$," or "y lies between x and z" (x, y, z being points on a line).

The distinction between a property and a (binary) relation can be pointed out by the following joke. A woman calls on her friend who has given birth to twins and says "your children are so beautiful, particularly the one on the left." Later, another friend calls and says "your children are so alike, particularly the one on the left." Grammatically, the sentences have the same structure, yet "beautiful" is a property, "alike" a relation.

The significance of the concept of one-to-one correspondence for the concept of *number*, meaning finite cardinal number, was pointed out by Descartes, and more strikingly by Hume.[3] (Another function of number, namely ordinal number, will be considered in Section 7.) For instance, the cardinal number 5 is common to all sets which are equivalent to the set of the fingers of one human hand, or equivalent to the set $\{0, 1, 2, 3, 4\}$. After having admitted the empty set $\emptyset$, we also have to admit the number 0, as the cardinal of $\emptyset$.

Although this idea seems to be clear and simple, it is nevertheless rather difficult to deduce the (finite) cardinals—coinciding with the non-negative integers—from the concepts of set and equivalence in a logically satisfactory manner. We only hint at the main points and for the rest refer the reader to the literature. In the following remarks *the finiteness of the sets concerned will not be used*. In Section 3 it will prove important that our arguments apply to *any* sets.

A natural formulation seems to be:

A. Equivalent sets have equal cardinals and, conversely, all sets with equal cardinals are equivalent.

Yet this might be considered unsatisfactory because it contains no explicit definition of cardinal (number).

Cantor tried to remedy this deficiency by means of a *definition through abstraction*,[4] as follows: The term "cardinal" signifies the concept which "through the process of thinking" is derived from a set S, by abstracting from the quality of the members of S and from the order in which they are given. The result of this double act of abstraction, the *cardinal* or *power* of S, is denoted by $\overline{\overline{S}}$[5].

---

[3] Cf. the following quotation from Hume's *Treatise of Human Nature* (Book I, Part III, Section 1): "When two numbers are so combined, that the one always has a unit answering to every unit of the other, we pronounce them equal, and it is for want of such a standard of quality in extension, that geometry can scarce be esteemed a perfect and infallible science." We shall see in Sections 3 and 6 how Cantor succeeded in obtaining such a "standard" for geometry also.

[4] The definitions through abstraction, essentially used already by Leibniz, constitute an important specialization of a general type of definition sometimes called "constructive mathematical definitions" [see Weyl (1949), pp. 8–13; cf. Pasch (1882), p. 40].

[5] Cantor (1932), p. 282 (first published in 1895).

The following definition would be logically preferable to this rather vague explanation:

B. The cardinal of S is the set of all sets that are equivalent to S.

This definition originated with Frege and Bertrand Russell.[6] But, unless special precautions are taken, for instance through a *theory of types* as introduced by Russell, it leads to contradictions of the kind described in Section 5. On the other hand, the use of a theory of types, which excludes these contradictions, is very inconvenient in practice.

But there are easier measures, notably Russell's *principle of abstraction,* which, contrary to its name, endeavors to avoid vague abstraction processes. It may be formulated as follows. Let R denote a symmetrical and transitive binary relation; then a one-to-many relation, R^* (of the father-child type), is defined by the rule that $x \, R \, y$ shall imply $z \, R^* \, x$ and $z \, R^* \, y$, where z is uniquely determined by x (or by y) but not conversely. (The existence of R^* can be proved by the methods of symbolic logic.) Then z is called the R-type of x, hence of any y that satisfies $y \, R \, x$.[7] For instance, if R means parallelism between (directed) straight lines, then z is the *direction* (of a line); if R means similarity between triangles, then z is the *shape* (of a triangle). According to this principle, the cardinal of a set S is the R-type of S (and of every equivalent set) if R means equivalence in the sense of Definition II.[7]

As for various objections that have been raised (in particular, by philosophers) against Definition A or B, there remains only the point regarding B that it would hardly be what is ordinarily meant by cardinal number, hence that the definition would not "hold." This objection shows a thorough misunderstanding of the nature of a definition. It is not a statement which may be true or false, but a stipulation which, in principle, is arbitrary and may turn out to be more or less useful. Definition B, in spite of its surprising character, can be used very easily. As to its abstract nature, this is shared by the definition of such concepts as "continuum," "dimension," and others. These concepts had been considered to be intuitively clear but, with the increasing development of science, they were found to require profound analysis. Incidentally, in analogy with B, *a real number is* defined as an infinite set of rational numbers.

---

[6] Frege (1884), §§63–68; Russell (1903), pp. 166 and 220; Whitehead-Russell (1910), 72.66. [Cf. Russell (1919).]

[7] Scholz-Schweitzer (1935) is a comprehensive monograph on definition through abstraction. It also includes a historical survey and a generalization to $2n$-ary relations for $n > 1$. For a modern exposition of the introduction of cardinals, using symbolic logic, see Carnap (1958), pp. 136–142.

Definition A does not explicitly establish what a cardinal *is*. However, from the mathematical point of view this is neither a rare occurrence nor an obstacle in developing a full-fledged theory of cardinals. As far as the first point is concerned, it is sufficient to refer to the *inductive* definitions in arithmetic and set theory (cf. Section 7), which are not explicit. Since the beginning of this century "functional" definitions have attained equal rights with material ("substantial") ones even in philosophy. The second point is more important. Mathematicians are not interested in the nature of their objects (numbers, functions, points, etc.) or in their metaphysical character. What matters are the relations and operations applying to the objects, in particular equality and order between them and rules for calculating with them—just as chess players are not interested in what a bishop "is" but in how it performs. In fact, definitions through abstraction are quite customary in modern mathematics.

In the present case, arranging the cardinals in the order of their "magnitude" and calculating with them can be reduced to the equality and inequality of cardinals, which is defined in A (see Sections 5 and 6). Hence Definition A, though simple, is sufficient for all purposes of mathematics.

Since in both Definition A and Definition B we have made no assumption about the finiteness of the sets involved, they are also suitable for defining the cardinals of infinite sets, usually called *transfinite cardinals*, in contrast to the finite cardinals 0, 1, 2, 3, $\cdots$. But the possibility of *defining* transfinite cardinals in this way does not imply that this concept has actual meaning. In the following section it will be shown that the concept is not trivial.

Section 3. Infinite Denumerable and Nondenumerable Sets. Transfinite Cardinals

In apparent contrast to what was stated on p. 1, in a certain sense infinity appeared in mathematics as an actual magnitude from the start, or at least at an early stage of Greek mathematics, when mathematics changed from an inductive science, as it had been developed and used by the peoples of the Middle East, into a deductive science. The statement $\lim_{n \to \infty} (1 / n) = 0$, whose essentially finite character was stressed on p. 1, actually refers to an infinite set, viz., to the sequence of all positive integers n. Similarly, Euclid's proof that after any prime number, within a definite interval, there exists a larger prime number, shows that the set of prime numbers is actually infinite. These concepts of infinity imply no vagueness: it has been proved that finitely many objects cannot exhaust these sets, and given any object o, one can ascertain unambiguously, and by means of a finite number of steps, whether or not o belongs to the set in question. The existence of these actually infinite sets, and of much more comprehensive ones, appears even more surprising nowadays than prior to the 20th century. Indeed, in the period of modern atomistics and of the Riemannian spaces of general relativity we have abandoned the belief in the indefinite divisibility of matter (or even of space) and in the actual infinitude of the universe. In short, nature seems to provide finite sets only.

We started with the *set of all positive integers* $N = \{1, 2, 3, \cdots, k, \cdots\}$. It is easy to produce infinite sets which are either less or more comprehensive. Examples of the first kind are the sets of all integers greater than 1, or greater than an arbitrary integer k, or of all prime numbers; for, every prime number is an integer but not conversely. There is even something surprising in Euclid's theorem because of the occurrence of indefinitely large gaps [1] in the sequence of the prime numbers, relative to N.

---

[1] In fact, however large the integer n, there are cases where no prime number is found among n successive integers. For instance, each of the n successive integers

$$(n + 1)! + 2, \ (n + 1)! + 3, \cdots, \ (n + 1)! + n, \ (n + 1)! + (n + 1),$$

where as usual $m!$ serves as an abbreviation for the product $1 \cdot 2 \cdot 3 \cdots \cdot m$, is clearly composite, i.e., not prime.

On the other hand, the set of *all* integers, including 0 and the negatives, or the set of all rationals (vulgar fractions l / k), belongs to the second kind. The latter set, where l assumes all integral and k all positive integral values, is even "*infinitely* more comprehensive" than N, in the sense that to every given member k of N there correspond the infinitely many rationals l / k (even if only those l are admitted that have no common divisor with k, thus producing "reduced" fractions).

However, these sets and others of a far more general nature, for instance the set of the algebraic numbers (p. 16), contribute nothing new to the problem of cardinals (see the end of Section 2). This follows from two elementary theorems which rest upon the definition of equivalence.

THEOREM 1.   *Any infinite subset N_0 of the set N of the positive integers is equivalent to N.*

To prove this we use the fact that in ny set of positive integers there is a *least* integer. Let us denote by n_1 the least number in N_0, by n_2 the least number in the remainder $N_1 = N_0 - \{n_1\}$ (i.e., in the set N_1 obtained from N_0 by omitting the number n_1), and so on. Generally, we denote by n_{k+1} the least number in the remainder $N_k = N_0 - \{n_1, n_2, \cdots, n_k\}$ for every $k = 0, 1, 2, \cdots$. Then no remainder N_k can be empty because this would mean that N_0 was finite. Hence we can continue selecting least numbers n_k *indefinitely* or, more precisely, corresponding to every positive integer k, and this procedure is completely determined. Thus we obtain the infinite set

$$\bar{N}_0 = \{n_1, n_2, \cdots, n_k, \cdots\},$$

which is certainly a *subset* of N_0; but $\bar{N}_0$ even *equals* N_0, since every element n of N_0 is a positive integer and the least in a certain remainder, namely, in the remainder obtained by omitting all integers less than n.

The equality $N_0 = \{n_1, n_2, \cdots, n_k, \cdots\}$ finally implies that N and N_0 are equivalent sets, in view of the mapping which assigns the element n_k of N_0 to the element k (i.e., to its index) of N.

To formulate the following theorem more easily, we introduce a definition which proves extremely useful in general.

DEFINITION I. Any set which is equivalent to the set N of all positive integers is called *denumerable* (or countable). A denumerable set is said to contain "denumerably many" members.

Hence any denumerable set D is infinite and can be written in the form[2]

$$D = \{d_1, d_2, d_3, \cdots, d_k, \cdots\},$$

where d_k is the element of D that is assigned to the integer k of N by a fixed (arbitrary) mapping of D onto N. A set which is equivalent to a denumerable set is also denumerable, in view of the transitivity of the equivalence relation; by Theorem 1, any infinite subset of a denumerable set is also denumerable.

THEOREM 2.   *A set which contains the elements of finitely many or of denumerably many denumerable sets is also denumerable.*

Proof.   Instead of taking denumerably many abstract sets, we choose an important concrete example which is nevertheless completely general, namely, *the set of all rationals $l \,/\, k$*, where $l \,/\, k$ may be assumed to be reduced (p. 13). If we first restrict l and k to *positive* integral values, then for a given k we have a denumerable set of rationals $l \,/\, k \,(l = 1, 2, \cdots)$; hence if k also assumes all positive integral values, we obtain a denumerable set of denumerable sets. To show that these sets together contain denumerably many members, we first arrange them in a sequence of rows according to fixed denominators k in the following scheme:

$$
\begin{array}{cccccc}
\dfrac{1}{1} \rightarrow & \dfrac{2}{1} & \dfrac{3}{1} \rightarrow & \dfrac{4}{1} & \dfrac{5}{1} \rightarrow & \cdot \quad \cdot \quad \cdot \\[2mm]
\dfrac{1}{2} & \dfrac{2}{2} & \dfrac{3}{2} & \dfrac{4}{2} & \cdot \\[2mm]
\dfrac{1}{3} & \dfrac{2}{3} & \dfrac{3}{3} & \cdot & \cdot \quad \cdot \quad \cdot \\[2mm]
\dfrac{1}{4} & \dfrac{2}{4} & \cdot & \cdot & \cdot \quad \cdot \quad \cdot \\[2mm]
\dfrac{1}{5} & \cdot & \cdot & \cdot & \cdot \quad \cdot \quad \cdot \\[2mm]
\cdot & \cdot & \cdot & \cdot & \cdot \quad \cdot \quad \cdot
\end{array}
$$

---

[2] There are two differences between a sequence (p.6) and a denumerable set: in a sequence, but not in a set, the same element may appear repeatedly, and a denumerable set is not necessarily ordered. If we order D according to the indices k, we speak of an *enumerated* set and write $(d_1, d_2, d_3, \cdots)$, which is indeed a sequence.

In the kth row there appear all the rationals with the denominator k, in the order $1/k$, $2/k$, $3/k$, $\cdots$.

Now we rearrange the rationals by following the arrows inserted in the scheme, beginning with $1/1$ and moving diagonally upward and downward in turn. Thus we obtain all the l/k as the elements of a single sequence. Finally we insert three modifications. First, before $1/1$ we put $0/1(=0)$. Second, each l/k shall be followed by the negative rational $-l/k$. Third, we omit all rationals which are equal to an earlier rational in our sequence, for instance $2/2(=1/1)$, $2/4(=1/2)$, etc. (The third step eliminates the rationals whose numerator and denominator have common divisors). Hence all distinct rationals are arranged in a sequence which shows that the set of all rationals is denumerable.

Clearly, this proof can be applied to any sequence of denumerable sets. Moreover, by Theorem 1 the result holds also for finitely many denumerable sets. In this case, however, a direct proof is much easier. (For instance, the set of *all* integers may be obtained as the union of N and of $\{0, -1, -2, \cdots\}$, and this union can be rearranged to read $\{0, 1, -1, 2, -2, 3, -3, \cdots\}$.) This completes the proof of Theorem 2.

Hence, in view of Theorem 1, *by adding finitely many elements to the elements of a denumerable set we again obtain a denumerable set.*

Theorems 1 and 2 suggest two conjectures: first, that any infinite set is equivalent to a proper subset of itself, and second, that any two infinite sets are equivalent to each other. However, only the first is true (though far from being self-evident); the second will prove false. We postpone to Section 4 the proof of the first conjecture, which involves certain difficulties, but we shall here prove the following special case:

THEOREM 3. *Any denumerable set is equivalent to a proper subset of itself.*

This is an immediate consequence of Theorem 1. For if

$$D = \{d_1, d_2, d_3, \cdots\}$$

is denumerable, then by Theorem 1 such sets as

$$\{d_2, d_3, d_4, \cdots\}, \quad \{d_k, d_{k+1}, d_{k+2}, \cdots\}, \quad \{d_1, d_3, d_5, \cdots\}, \quad \text{etc.,}$$

proper subsets of D, are also denumerable, i.e., they are equivalent to D. The equivalence between the set of the positive integers on the one hand and the set of the integers greater than 1, or the even positive integers, on the other, may be illustrated by the following mappings:

$$
\begin{array}{ccccccc}
2 & 3 & 4 & \cdots & k+1 & k+2 & \cdots \\
\updownarrow & \updownarrow & \updownarrow & \updownarrow & \updownarrow & \updownarrow & \updownarrow \\
1 & 2 & 3 & \cdots & k & k+1 & \cdots \\
\updownarrow & \updownarrow & \updownarrow & \updownarrow & \updownarrow & \updownarrow & \updownarrow \\
2 & 4 & 6 & \cdots & 2k & 2k+2 & \cdots
\end{array}
$$

Theorem 3 contradicts a famous principle formulated by Greek philosophers and mathematicians, namely, the principle that the whole is greater than its parts—in its Latin form, *totum parte maius*. This principle has played an important role in medieval and modern philosophy. Yet according to A on p. 9, the set D and certain proper subsets of D— in fact, *all* infinite subsets of D—have the same cardinal. This supposed paradox, pointed out by Galileo in the early 17th century, still proved an obstacle two hundred years later for as modern a thinker as Bolzano (p. 2) in his efforts to develop a theory of infinity. A few decades later, however, it was used for the very *definition* of infinity (see Section 4).

As far as the second conjecture mentioned above is concerned, we shall first strengthen it by additional examples and arguments before we finally refute it (p. 20).

The first example is of a special nature and requires some computational technique. It is inserted here because of its great significance in arithmetic (cf. p. 24). We shall present it in a brief form, adapted to experienced readers.

Any root of an algebraic equation of a positive degree n,

$$
(1) \qquad a_0x^n + a_1x^{n-1} + \cdots + a_{n-1}x + a_n = 0 \qquad (a_0 \neq 0),
$$

with integral coefficients a_k is called an *algebraic number*. For simplicity we restrict ourselves to *real* algebraic numbers. It is easily shown that (1) has *at most* n real roots.

We arrange all equations of the form (1) not according to the degrees n or the magnitude of the coefficients, but according to the magnitude of the positive integer

$$
h = (n-1) + |a_0| + |a_1| + \cdots + |a_{n-1}| + |a_n|,
$$

which we call the height of the equation; $|a|$ means, as usual, the absolute value of a. Clearly h is uniquely defined by (1). It is easily seen that, conversely, only finitely many equations (1) with height h correspond to a given h. (To prove this, we first observe that the degree n of (1) cannot be greater than h, and then arrange the equations of the height h according to their degrees.)

By arranging the equations of given height in an arbitrary way and those of different heights h by increasing values of h, we obtain a *sequence* which contains all equations (1), each at a certain fixed place. Finally, every equation (with real roots) is replaced by its finitely many roots, which may be arranged arbitrarily. Thus we obtain an *enumeration* of all real algebraic numbers (from which, to avoid repetition, we may omit those which equal earlier numbers). Hence

THEOREM 4.   *The set of all real algebraic numbers is denumerable.*

This theorem includes the denumerability of the rationals, for the rationals are the algebraic numbers of degree $n - 1$, namely the roots of $a_0 x + a = 0$.

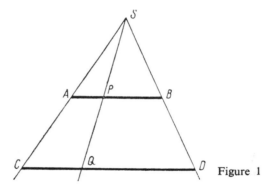

Figure 1

The two following examples refer to (straight) segments or lines, which will be regarded as the sets of all points lying on the segment or the line. In Figure 1 two segments $\overline{AB}$ and $\overline{CD}$ are drawn, $\overline{CD}$ longer than $\overline{AB}$. Nevertheless, the set of points $\overline{AB}$ is *equivalent* to the set of points $\overline{CD}$. To prove this, we draw the segments parallel to each other, as in Figure 1, and connect C and A, as well as D and B, by straight lines which, because of the different lengths of the segments, intersect in a point S. Any ray drawn from S intersects either both segments or neither of them. In the former case, for instance, in the case of the ray SP, the intersection of the ray with $\overline{CD}$, namely the point Q, shall be assigned to the intersection of the ray with $\overline{AB}$, i.e., to the point P, and conversely. Thus we obtain a one-to-one correspondence between the points of both sets, which shows that these sets are equivalent.

A still more surprising result is obtained if one of the segments is replaced by a full straight line (Figure 2). Here we have drawn a segment $\overline{AB}$ beneath an infinite line DE. We shall see that the set of points $\overline{AB}$, excluding the end-points A and B, is equivalent to the set of *all* points of the line. To prove this we denote the center of $\overline{AB}$ by C, bend the segment (as though it were a thin wire) at C, and lay it upon the line in such a way that C becomes a point of DE, and A and B lie on the same side of the line (in Figure 2, above it) and at an equal distance from it. Finally, we denote by S the midpoint of the the new positions of A and B.

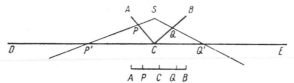

Figure 2

Clearly, any ray drawn from S either intersects both the (bent) segment and the line, or intersects neither. (The rays SA and SB are parallel to the line, hence do not intersect it. For this reason we have excluded the end-points A and B of the segment.) Now we assign any point of the bent segment, for instance P or Q, to the point P' or Q', respectively, in which the ray SP or SQ intersects the line, and conversely; in particular, the point C is then assigned to itself. Thus we have established a mapping of $\overline{AB}$ onto the set of all points of the line DE, which shows that even these seemingly quite unequal sets are equivalent.

Readers who are familiar with the elements of trigonometry may grasp the essence of the last example in a simple analytic way. The function tan x is monotonically increasing in the open interval from $x = -\pi/2$ ($-90°$) to $x = \pi/2$ ($90°$) and assumes all real values in this interval. Hence this function establishes a mapping of the finite interval ($-\pi/2, \pi/2$) onto the set of all real numbers.

The last examples show most impressively how a set may be equivalent to a part of itself, even to a seemingly infinitesimal part.[3] Thus the conjecture

---

[3] This phenomenon seems even more paradoxical when it is transferred, so to speak, to real life—the "reality" being fictitious, of course. This applies to the story of *Tristram Shandy*, who writes his autobiography so pedantically that the description of each single day takes him a year. If he is mortal he can never finish it. But if he could live forever, then no part of his biography would remain unwritten, for to each day of his life there would correspond a year devoted to that day's description.

expressed on p. 15, that *all* infinite sets might be equivalent, gains additional weight. If this conjecture, which up to the 1870's had been tacitly assumed to be self-evident, proved to be true, then the concept of cardinal number would not be significant for infinite sets.

The method of mapping an infinite set *S* onto a proper subset, as applied above several times, has sometimes been criticized by philosophers with the argument that every element of *S* should be assigned *to itself* in a subset of *S*, provided the element belongs to the subset. If this argument were justified, then immediately the first and simplest of our examples, namely, the mapping of $\{1, 2, 3, \cdots\}$ onto $\{2, 3, 4, \cdots\}$, would be invalid, because the element 1 of the first set would remain without an image in the second. In general it is clear that no proof of equivalence between a set and a proper subset of itself can be carried out by assigning elements to themselves. In the case of Figure 1, for instance, the mapping ought then to be carried out by means of *parallels* to one of the lines *AC, BD*, instead of by *rays* from *S*, and the aim would not be attained. Thus the principle of *totum parte maius* would be saved.

However, the postulate of assigning elements to themselves by means of "identical" correspondence is quite arbitrary and unfounded; it purposely ignores the definition of equivalence. As far as the members of equivalent infinite sets are concerned it is certainly always possible to relate them in a way that will *not* yield a mapping, just as in general it is easy to *fail to solve* a given mathematical problem by applying unsuitable methods. Failure will usually result from tackling the problem inexpediently, and will not be an indication of its insolubility.

To prove that a problem is *unsolvable*—in the present case, that two sets are *not equivalent*—it must be shown that *any possible method* of solution (here, of mapping) necessarily leads to failure. Such "impossibility proofs" are difficult as a rule; we shall soon present such a proof (of the Fundamental Theorem).

The blunder committed by the critics is caused by an erroneous generalization of an (empirical and logical) observation regarding *finite* sets. In fact, for two finite sets, the failure of an *arbitrary* attempt at mapping the one onto the other implies that *any* such attempt is bound to be unsuccessful; cf. Section 4, Theorem 3, and Section 7, p. 77.

But now we have arrived at a critical junction. Either we do succeed in constructing infinite sets which are not equivalent, and hence obtain different infinite cardinals; or else, if any two infinite sets are equivalent, then the theory of sets that are actually infinite, and of their cardinals, proves to be trivial and the definition of equivalence and cardinal are significant for finite sets only.

We shall now prove the proposition that the former alternative holds, by exhibiting an infinite set which is not denumerable, i.e., a set that is not equivalent to the set of the positive integers. It is only when we reach this result that we have a proper basis for the theory of sets. It was the earliest (1873) achievement in set theory by Cantor (with a proof more complicated than the one below). Cantor, to be sure, was not yet conscious of the fundamental nature of his discovery.

The set in question is well known to us; we may take it to be the "continuum" of all points of the segment $\overline{AB}$ in Figure 1 (p. 17). As was shown there, this continuum is equivalent to the continuum of the points of *any* finite segment or of the infinite line. To express our proposition in a form which is easy to prove, we use the one-to-one correspondence between all points of a line and all real numbers that is well-known from diagrams[4] or from analytic geometry. This correspondence includes the correspondence between the points of a *segment* and the real numbers of an *interval* (i.e., the numbers x which satisfy the inequalities $a \leq x \leq b$); if the segment lacks one or both end-points the $\leq$ must be replaced, correspondingly, by $<$. In view of this correspondence we may regard the continuum as a set of real numbers, and any of the above sets of points or numbers will be referred to as *the continuum*. The definite article is justified since all these sets are equivalent and we shall be dealing only with equivalence properties. Hence we may formulate our proposition as follows:

FUNDAMENTAL THEOREM. *The denumerable set N of all positive integers is not equivalent to the continuum but only to a proper subset of the continuum. In other words, the continuum is a more-than-denumerable set.*

The second statement is evident in view of Theorem 2 (p. 14; cf. its interpretation by means of the rational numbers), for the continuum includes infinitely many rational numbers, whose totality is equivalent to N.

To prove the theorem we take as our continuum the particular interval from 0 to 1 and denote it by C. First we shall represent its elements (real numbers) in a convenient way, namely, as *decimals* (decimal fractions). For this purpose we shall use an elementary theorem about decimals which states that *every positive real number can be expanded in one, and only one, way into an "infinite" decimal*, i.e., into a decimal that after any digit contains yet another digit differing from 0. (There are positive numbers which admit an expansion into a terminating decimal, for instance $\frac{3}{4} = 0.75$; but then there also exists an infinite expansion, in our case $\frac{3}{4} = 0.74999\cdots$

---

4 This one-to-one correspondence is not self-evident; it is based, on the one hand, on a full analysis of the geometric nature of a line (in particular, the so-called Dedekind-Cantor axiom or Hilbert's axiom of completeness) and, on the other hand, on an arithmetical definition of irrational and real numbers. We shall not expound these theories here, but regard this correspondence as being intuitively clear.

Anyone who finds this surprising may multiply the well-known expansion $1/9 = 0.111\cdots$ by 9, thus obtaining $1 = 0.999\cdots$) Since all decimal fractions of C begin with $0.\cdots$, we shall include the number 1 ($= 0.999\cdots$) in C, but we shall not include the number 0, which cannot be represented by a non-terminating decimal fraction; then C is exactly the set of all infinite decimal fractions beginning with $0.\cdots$.

The fundamental theorem asserts that a set equivalent to N, i.e., a denumerable set, cannot contain *all* decimals of C. We prove this "in-directly" by assuming that C is denumerable and deriving a contradiction from this assumption. (For a "direct" version of this proof see below.) If C were denumerable, we could choose a definite mapping of C onto N which relates every decimal of C to a positive integer n and conversely; for brevity we call the decimal related to n "the nth decimal" and we may then speak of the first, the second, $\cdots$ decimal. Therefore, according to our assumption, we can write the elements of the continuum C as a sequence:

$$0.n_{11}\,n_{12}\,n_{13}\,n_{14}\cdots$$
$$\searrow$$
$$0.n_{21}\,n_{22}\,n_{23}\,n_{24}\cdots$$
$$\searrow$$
$$0.n_{31}\,n_{32}\,n_{33}\,n_{34}\cdots$$
$$\searrow$$
$$0.n_{41}\,n_{42}\,n_{43}\,n_{44}\cdots$$
$$\vdots$$

where all n_{ik} ($i, k = 1, 2, \cdots$) are *digits*, i.e., numerals between 0 and 9, inclusive. If we disregard the common initial 0, we have here an infinite square of digits with the vertex n_{11}, which spreads to the right and downward; in particular, no "row" of the square can finally consist of zeros only, since all the decimals are infinite. For any digit n_{ik}, the first index, i, stands for the ith row of the square, and the second index, k, for its kth column; n_{ik} is then the kth digit of the ith decimal of C. For instance, n_{75} is the fifth digit of the seventh decimal.

We shall now specify an infinite (uniquely defined) decimal d beginning with 0, hence a member of C, which is not contained in the infinite square; that is to say, there exists no integer i such that d is the ith decimal of C. To construct d, we consider the diagonal of the square which passes through the digits $n_{11}, n_{22}, \cdots, n_{ii}, \cdots$ (cf. the arrows inserted in the square). d is the infinite decimal

$$d = 0.d_1 d_2 \cdots d_i \cdots$$

whose digits are defined as follows. For any i for which n_{ii} is different from the numeral 1, $d_i = 1$; for those i for which $n_{ii} = 1, d_i = 2$. Hence, always, $d_i \neq n_{ii}$; that is to say, for every i, d_i is different from the ith digit of the ith decimal.

The member d of C is therefore not contained in our square, which was assumed to contain all infinite decimals beginning with 0, i.e., all positive real numbers up to the number 1. We have thus obtained a contradiction, which shows that our assumption that the continuum C is equivalent to the set N of integers is untenable. Thus the proof of the Fundamental Theorem is complete.[5]

Remarks on the proof of the Fundamental Theorem. Although the proof given here presents no technical difficulty, it raises several questions of principle whose character is logical rather than mathematical. It is worth dealing with these questions, particularly since the Fundamental Theorem is one of the most important and most applicable theorems of mathematics and since it has been attacked by philosophers, and also by some mathematicians and physicists,[6] more often than any other mathematical theorem, with the possible exception of the well-ordering theorem (see Section 7).

(1) The indirect procedure of our proof has been adopted for psychological reasons only, namely, to make it more comprehensible. It will become a *direct* proof if we delete the assumption that the denumerable set C contains *all* the decimals involved. Then the construction of the decimal d shows that *no denumerable set of decimals can contain all decimals of the type in question*, and this coincides with the statement of the Fundamental Theorem.

(2) In Section 4 we shall deal with the basic difference between *constructive* and *existential* proofs or propositions, the former being logically

---

[5] This is esssentially the proof given by Cantor in 1892 [see Cantor (1932), pp. 278–280]. Cantor's first proof of 1873 is more complicated; it is contained in the same paper [Cantor (1932), p.117] in which he proved the denumerability of the set of the algebraic numbers (see above, p. 17). Another remarkable proof of the Fundamental Theorem was given by H. Poincaré [Poincaré (1910), pp. 45 f.].

[6] Compare, for instance, Bridgman (1934), Fraenkel (1935b), Kreisel (1950).

superior to the latter. Our proof has constructive character. To stress this, we have specialized in an exaggerated measure by favoring the numerals 1 and 2. In fact, it would have been sufficient to choose the digits d_i of d by prescribing that d_i *shall differ from* n_{ii} *and from* 0 (the latter to prevent d from becoming a terminating decimal which might represent the same real number as one of the decimals of our square). Our arbitrary specialization shows that one can construct a uniquely defined d in the above manner or in infinitely many other ways. (Cf. pp. 42f.) We have adopted this procedure in order to dispel the illusion, associated with some presentations of the proof, that the method is purely existential i.e., that it merely shows that there exist decimals like d, without leading to the construction of such decimals.

(3) In view of the decisive part that the diagonal members n_{ii} play in our proof—which is essentially true for any proof of the Theorem—this method of proof is called *Cantor's diagonal process*. It is one of the most powerful and famous methods of mathematics, and is used at various junctures in set theory (cf. the proof of "Cantor's theorem" in Section 5). In the present case the diagonal method characterizes the gulf that separates the discrete character of the set N of integers from the continuous character of the set C of the real numbers (points); in other words, the gulf that separates arithmetic from analysis and geometry. Arithmetic deals with individuals (the integers); geometry and analysis deal with the homogeneity of space, which is also reflected in the theory of (continuous) functions.

(4) Despite its rather simple character and the absence of computations, the argument in our proof is fundamentally more profound than the arguments in earlier proofs in the present section, such as those of Theorems 1 through 4 and those illustrated by Figures 1 and 2. The reason is simple. In the latter proofs the point was to find a certain mapping between two sets. This may require a certain amount of skill, but once the construction has been arrived at, we have completed our task. To prove the Fundamental Theorem, on the other hand, we have to show that *any* attempt at constructing a mapping is bound to end in failure; in other words, we need an *impossibility proof*.

As one may expect, and as is confirmed in various branches of mathematics, impossibility proofs are generally more profound than mere constructions. It is characteristic that even the Greeks, whose positive achievements in geometry are so admirable, sensed the impossibility of solving other geometrical problems but were not able to prove the-impossibility. All these "classical" impossibility theorems of geometry were established only in the 19th century; we mention in particular the impossibility (by means of ruler and compasses only) of duplicating the cube, trisecting the angle, constructing the regular heptagon, squaring the circle (this problem is more profound than the others because π is transcendental; see below), and also the impossibility of proving Euclid's axiom of parallels.

(5) The constructive nature of our proof has an important consequence in connection with Theorem 4 (p. 17). Any real (or complex) number that is not algebraic is called *transcendental.* Up to the middle of the 19th century it was unknown whether transcendental numbers existed at all. The most famous ones are e (the base of the natural logarithms) and π (the constant occurring in computations dealing with the circle). Our theorems show *not only that there are infinitely many real transcendental numbers but that there are more-than-denumerably many.* Indeed the set of all real numbers is, by definition, the union of the set A of real algebraic numbers and of the set T of real transcendental numbers. By Theorem 4, A is denumerable; hence if T were finite or denumerable then, by Theorem 2, the set of all real numbers would also be denumerable, contrary to the Fundamental Theorem. One may then say that "ordinarily" a real number is transcendental and only "exceptionally" algebraic—although almost all individual numbers we normally deal with are algebraic. Thus the power of Cantor's result, however simple the resources of its proof may be, is strikingly illustrated by a mathematical problem which is not connected with set theory at all.

Moreover, theoretically we have here even a method of *constructing* transcendental numbers, in view of the constructive definition of d and of similar numbers. For this purpose we choose the denumerable set, represented in our infinite square, as the set of all real algebraic numbers. Then every "diagonal" element, such as d [cf. in (2) above], is transcendental.

(6) Sometimes the following objection is raised against the Fundamental Theorem and its proof. The indirect method [or the direct method presented in (1)] depends on the fact that the decimal d [like many others, according to (2)] is not contained in the denumerable set from which we started. Yet, as shown by Theorems 2, 3, 4 at the beginning of this section, the addition of finitely many, or denumerably many, new members to those contained in a denumerable set does not change the fact that the latter is denumerable. Is not our proof, then, insufficient for the purpose of showing that the continuum is not denumerable?

Raising this objection (and it has sometimes been raised) means committing a blunder in logic which is allied with a misunderstanding of the very essence of our proof. In fact, on p. 21 we started with *any* denumerable set of decimals; the assumption that this set contains all members of the continuum then yields the contradiction. Therefore the construction of a single extraneous decimal d is sufficient; whether the addition of d or other decimals to our denumerable set will again produce a denumerable set is an idle question, because any denumerable set whatsoever answers the purpose.

To be sure, there is some connection between this erroneous objection and Richard's paradox; we shall raise this question on p. 53.

(7) The use of *decimal* fractions, i.e., of the base 10, in the proof is of course unimportant. The use of the decadic scale of notation, including decimals, in our civilization (in contrast to the older civilizations of Mesopotamia and other peoples, where 6, 12, etc. were used as bases) does not rest on mathematical considerations but on the biological fact that man has ten fingers (and that primitive man used his fingers for reckoning). Binary fractions (base 2) or "system fractions" with any base greater than ? serve our purpose as well, although for the base 2 a slightly more complicated procedure is needed in order to avoid terminating decimals.

The Fundamental Theorem finally refutes the conjecture that all infinite sets might be equivalent. Therefore, by the definitions of equivalence and cardinal in Section 2, we have to assign a certain transfinite cardinal to all denumerable sets (e.g., to the set of integers) and a different cardinal to the continuum. The main point is that *there exist different transfinite cardinals.* Cantor, who was at a loss for new symbols to designate the transfinite cardinals, chose $\aleph$ (aleph), the first letter of the Hebrew alphabet, and this notation has been accepted universally; to distinguish different alephs, indices are added. Thus the cardinal of denumerable sets, which will prove to be the *least* cardinal, is written $\aleph_0$ (aleph-zero). The cardinal of the continuum is denoted (following Hausdorff) by $\aleph$ without an index, for it proves to be extremely difficult (see pp. 37 and 89), or even impossible, to ascertain the position of this cardinal among the others. Yet we shall certainly be able to say (on the basis of a definition of inequality, see p. 41) that $\aleph_0$ is *smaller* than $\aleph$, in view of the fact that, by the Fundamental Theorem, the set of integers is equivalent to a subset of the continuum but not to the continuum itself.

With the definition of different transfinite cardinals—at present, of two such cardinals—we have taken the first decisive step in set theory. However, before taking further steps we shall give an account of the difficulties in logic brought about by this step.

Section 4. Logical Problems of Finiteness and Infinity.
The Axiom of Choice

So far we have defined the finiteness of a *set* by means of the concept of finite *number* (integer; see p. 4). In this sense we shall more specifically call a finite set, including the null set, an *inductive set*, referring to mathematical induction[1] (sometimes called "inference from n to $n + 1$"), which is characteristic of the theory of positive integers, and hence also of inductive sets. Bertrand Russell has shown that the explicit reference to integers can be eliminated[2] from this definition of finite sets, and Tarski presented several definitions, seemingly quite different, which can be proved to be logically equivalent to the definition of an "inductive" set and to each other in an elementary sense, namely, without use of the axiom of choice [see Tarski (1925)].

Yet there are other, fundamentally different definitions of finiteness and infinity; we shall now examine one to which we have already referred on p. 15. Surprisingly enough, this will lead us to a novel logico-mathematical problem which for sixty years caused difficulties and heated discussions in the world of science and which was finally solved, rather unexpectedly, in 1963.

We start with a theorem which looks quite harmless but which actually conceals far-reaching depths:

THEOREM 1. *Every infinite set I includes a denumerable subset.*

Proof. In accordance with the above concept of finiteness we here consider "infinite" to mean "noninductive." The theorem will be proved by mathematical induction, as is usual in arithmetic.

---

1 The principle of mathematical induction may be expressed briefly as follows: a set which contains the member 1 and which, together with any element n, also contains $n + 1$, contains *all* positive integers. (By replacing 1 by 0, we obtain the non-negative integers.)

2 Viz. by the following definitions: (a) a set of cardinals is called *hereditary* if the fact that it contains n implies that it contains $n + 1$; (b) a cardinal is called *inductive* if it belongs to every hereditary set that contains 1; (c) a set is called *inductive* if its cardinal is inductive. [Note that $n + 1$ in (a) is taken in the sense of union, i.e., of adding elements.] Cf. the references in footnote 6 on p. 10.

We start by choosing an arbitrary element i_1 of the nonempty set I, and form the subset $S_1 = \{i_1\}$ of I which contains a single element. The remainder, $I_1 = I - S_1$, is not empty, since otherwise I would contain one element only and not infinitely many; therefore we may choose an arbitrary element i_2 of I_1 and form the subset $S_2 = \{i_1, i_2\}$ of I which contains two elements. We may now inductively assume that after n such steps (n denoting any positive integer) we have arrived at a subset $S_n = \{i_1, i_2, \cdots, i_n\}$ of I which contains n elements. Since the remainder, $I_n = I - S_n$, is still infinite, we can choose an arbitrary element i_{n+1} of I_n; by adding it to the elements of S_n we obtain a subset $S_{n+1} = \{i_1, i_2, \cdots, i_n, i_{n+1}\}$ of I which contains $n+1$ elements. Hence, by the induction principle, for *any* positive integer n there exists a subset S_n of I which contains just n members; these subsets form an infinite sequence $(S_1, S_2, \cdots, S_n, \cdots)$. Moreover, they have been chosen so that any S_n includes the preceding ones; that is to say, $S_m \subset S_n$ for $m < n$.

Finally, the union $\bar{I}$ of all sets S_n contains denumerably many (possibly even all) members of I, namely,

$$\bar{I} = \{i_1, i_2, \cdots, i_n, \cdots\}.$$

Since $\bar{I}$ is a denumerable subset of I, Theorem 1 has been proved.
The proof has deliberately (cf. below) been carried out rather pedantically. In fact, its technique is extremely simple. We choose any element I and, after having chosen n elements, we choose one more. All the chosen elements together, corresponding to all the positive integers n, constitute a denumerable subset of I, in accordance with Theorem 1.

Now we are ready to prove the result announced on p. 15, namely,

THEOREM 2. *Any infinite set I is equivalent to a proper subset of I.*

Proof. Let $\bar{I}$ be an (arbitrary) denumerable subset of I; it exists, by Theorem 1. We denote the remainder, $I - \bar{I}$, by I'; if $\bar{I}$ coincides with I, then I' is the null set. In any case, we have $I = \bar{I} \cup I'$, $\bar{I}$ and I' being disjoint sets. Now omit the member i_1 from the denumerable set $\bar{I} = \{i_1, i_2, i_3, \cdots\}$ and denote the remainder $\bar{I} - \{i_1\}$ by $\bar{I}_1$; then $\bar{I}_1 \cup I' = I_1$ is a proper subset of I, because I_1 does not contain the member i_1 of I. Moreover, $\bar{I}_1$ and I' are disjoint.

We now set up a mapping of $I = \bar{I} \cup I'$ onto its proper subset $I_1 = \bar{I}_1 \cup I'$ in the following way. Every member of I', if any, is to be assigned to itself; in fact, we have no alternative to this identical mapping, since we do not know whether I' is empty, finite, or infinite. On the other hand, a mapping of $\bar{I}$ onto $\bar{I}_1$ is given by the following scheme, which is analogous to those on p. 16:

$$\bar{I}: \quad i_1 \quad\quad i_2 \;\cdots\; i_{n-1} \quad\quad i_n$$

$$\updownarrow \quad\;\; \updownarrow \quad\;\; \updownarrow \quad\quad\;\; \updownarrow$$

$$\bar{I}_1: \quad i_2 \quad\quad i_3 \;\cdots\; i_n \quad\quad\;\; i_{n+1}$$

Both mappings together yield a mapping of I onto I_1, which completes the proof of Theorem 2.

More simply, this proof runs as follows. After having split the given infinite set into a denumerable subset (Theorem 1) and the (possibly empty) remainder, the latter is mapped identically onto itself, and the former onto a proper subset of itself (conveniently a subset obtained by omitting a single element). Hence the original set is mapped onto a proper subset of itself.

Example : Let I be the set of all rational numbers, $\bar{I}$ the set of all positive integers. Then we may take for $\bar{I}_1$ the set of all integers greater than 1, and I_1 becomes the set of all rationals that differ from 1.

THEOREM 3. *A finite set F cannot be equivalent to a proper subset of itself.*

This theorem is well known even to children, by their experience in playing. Actually, it is a theorem of arithmetic and is proved by the typical method of arithmetic, viz., mathematical induction. It will be sufficient to outline the proof. The theorem is self-evident if F contains only a single member. Assuming the theorem to be true for any F containing n members, we easily conclude that it is also true for any set with $n+1$ members. Hence it is true for every finite (inductive) set.

By Theorems 2 and 3, the classification of sets into finite (inductive) or infinite (noninductive) sets coincides with their classification into sets which are or are not equivalent to a proper subset of themselves. For brevity we shall (with Russell) call *reflexive* any set which is equivalent to a proper subset of itself.

We now give another proof of Theorem 1, where we understand "infinite" in the sense of "reflexive." The new proof is fundamentally different from the old one, both technically and in principle. This is not surprising, for we shall see that we are dealing with basically different theorems, according to whether infinite means "noninductive" or "reflexive."

We shall give the proof of Theorem 1 (in the new sense) in a form adapted for experienced readers. Let the reflexive set R be equivalent to the proper subset $\bar{R} \subset R$, and let φ be an arbitrary mapping of R onto $\bar{R}$, and r_1 an arbitrary element of the remainder $R - \bar{R}$. Then φ assigns

the element r_1 of R to an element r_2 of $\bar{R}$,

the element r_2 of R to an element r_3 of $\bar{R}$,

$$\vdots$$

the element r_n of R to an element r_{n+1} of $\bar{R}$.

$$\vdots$$

After the (arbitrary) choice of r_1 and of the mapping φ, all the elements $r_2, r_3, \cdots, r_n, \cdots$ of R are uniquely determined and form an infinite sequence. Each of them, *except* r_1 which belongs to $R - \bar{R}$, also belongs to $\bar{R}$.

To complete the proof, we still have to show that any two r_n with distinct indices n are themselves distinct. We show this indirectly. If they are not all distinct, let r_m be the *first* r_n which equals a previous one, say r_k; that is to say

$$r_m = r_k \qquad (k < m, \text{ hence } m > 1).$$

Because $m > 1$, r_m belongs to $\bar{R}$ and is therefore *distinct from* r_1; hence r_k is also distinct from r_1, i.e., $k > 1$. Therefore r_k is assigned to an element r_{k-1} of R by φ, as is r_m to an r_{m-1}, and since φ defines a one-to-one correspondence, $r_m = r_k$ implies $r_{m-1} = r_{k-1}$. But this contradicts our assumption that m is the least index for which r_m equals a previous element. This contradiction shows that all the r_n are distinct.

Therefore,

$$\{r_1, r_2, \cdots, r_n, \cdots\}$$

is a denumerable subset of R and the proof is complete.

Before continuing, the reader is advised to ponder on which proof he considers simpler (and why), the one given now or the previous proof of Theorem 1 (p. 27), where "infinite" meant "noninductive."

Thus we have two definitions of the pair of concepts "finite, infinite" (sets) at our disposal, namely, "inductive, noninductive" and "nonreflexive, reflexive." It makes no difference that "finite" is defined negatively in the second procedure, for this definition can also be formulated as follows: a set F is finite if the existence of a mapping of F onto a subset F' of F implies $F' = F$.

We shall now examine in detail the (first) proof of Theorem 1. A comparison of this proof with the arguments found in both ancient and modern mathematics shows a striking difference. The concepts used in traditional proofs are, generally, uniquely determined. True, an opposite impression is often created: for instance, the proof of a certain property of isosceles triangles starts with the phrase "let ABC be any isosceles triangle" (after it has been shown that such triangles exist). Expressed in the language of set theory, this means that when a set S has been shown not to be empty we are entitled to "choose" an arbitrary element of S; in other words, to say "let s be an arbitrary element of S" or "let $\{s\}$ be a set that contains a single element of S." This presupposes that the succeeding arguments are independent of the particular member chosen.[3]

From the choice of a single element we may proceed by mathematical induction (p. 26) to choose a finite number, say k, of elements of S, provided the set S contains at least k elements.

On the other hand, within the framework of the logical and mathematical procedures which were usual and recognized up to the end of the 19th century, *one is not permitted to take infinitely many steps in choosing arbitrary elements which are not determined by a definite law* (see below). This exclusion of an infinity of choices is based by some critics on the argument that any logical procedure must be brought to an end within a finite length of time, which would apparently be impossible in this case. Yet this argument is hardly tenable, for the process of thinking should be regarded as instantaneous and not as taking a definite length of time. (Anyone who disagrees with this attitude may carry out an infinite sequence of choices within a finite period of time by allotting half a minute to the first choice, $1/4$ minute to the second, $\cdots$, $1/2^n$ minute to the nth choice, whereby all the choices for $n=1, 2, \cdots$ would be "completed" within one minute.)

Yet a deeper analysis shows that procedures involving infinitely many arbitrary steps have been avoided in the past not for the reason mentioned above, but because they were considered to be *meaningless*, not merely nonconstructive. This attitude was generally adopted implicitly or subconsciously. Even in 1890, when the well-known mathematician and logician G. Peano was dealing with a certain problem in differential equations, he explicitly refrained from an easy solution by means of an infinity

---

[3] A more rigorous formulation is given in the so-called Deduction Theorem; cf. Hilbert-Bernays (1934), p. 155.

of choices and, instead, developed a constructive method with the express argument : *Mais comme on ne peut pas appliquer une infinité de fois une loi arbitraire avec laquelle à une classe on falt correspondre un individu de cette classe, on a formé ici une loi déterminée avec laquelle à chaque classe, sous des hypothèses convenables, on fait correspondre un individu de cette classe.*[4]

Naturally, systems of infinitely many simultaneous correspondences are a matter of course in mathematics, or may even be considered to be *characteristic* of mathematics. Thus the function $y = x^2$ puts every real number x into correspondence with its square x^2; the function "the least number of the set a" puts every nonempty set of positive integers into correspondence with a well-defined element of the set. In such cases, which occur in all mathematics, a *law* (function) defines the correspondence simultaneously for infinitely many cases and in a constructive way. However in the original proof of Theorem 1 (p. 27) there is *no law at our disposal* for choosing the elements i_{n+1} ($n = 1, 2, 3, \cdots$), and it is doubtful whether such a law exists. All we know about the successive remainders I_n is that they are infinite (and therefore nonempty) sets, which is enough to choose an i_{n+1} out of each I_n.

As far as the second proof, given on p. 29, is concerned, the situation is quite different. Here only a single act of choice is required, namely the choice of an arbitrary element r_1 from the nonempty set $R - \bar{R}$. All the other elements r_2, r_3, $\cdots$ of R are then uniquely defined by the mapping of R onto $\bar{R}$. Thus it seems that this proof is a simpler and more elementary proof of Theorem 1 than the original one. Yet this is a delusion. Certainly the proof is more elementary, but it is the proof of another, weaker theorem. As we shall see presently, Theorem 1 with "infinite" = "noninductive" is a far stronger statement than with "infinite" = "reflexive." It is not surprising then that the weaker statement can be proved more simply, in fact in an essentially constructive way.[5]

The difference between the definition of a subset by comprehension, i.e., by a property that is characteristic of the elements of the subset,

---

4 "Yet, since one cannot apply infinitely often an arbitrary procedure which assigns an individual element of the set to a given set, we have here established a definite law which under suitable assumptions assigns an individual element of the set to every given set." [See Peano (1890), p. 210.]

5 Obviously an assertion (here, the existence of a denumerable subset of I) generally says *less* (hence can be more easily proved) if its hypothesis (here, the infiniteness of I) is *stronger*.

and its definition by infinitely many arbitrary choices (as in the original proof of Theorem 1), can be illustrated in an almost graphic way by an example by Bertrand Russell given at the very beginning of these discussions. (It is "almost" graphic because the assumption of infinity involved in it cannot be actually realized.)

Imagine a denumerable set whose elements are *pairs of shoes*: a first, second, $\cdots$, nth, $\cdots$ pair for every positive integer n. Is the set of all these *pairs* equivalent to the set of all *shoes* contained in the pairs? The answer is, of course, in the affirmative. As in the case of the set of all integers (p. 15), we may assign to the first pair, the left shoe of the first pair; to the second pair, the right shoe of the first pair; to the third pair, the left shoe of the second pair, and so on. Then the left shoe of the nth pair corresponds to the $(2n-1)$st pair, the right shoe of the nth pair to the $(2n)$th pair. Evidently this rule yields a mapping of the set of all pairs onto the set of all shoes, hence the sets are equivalent: there are $\aleph_0$ pairs and $\aleph_0$ shoes.

However, the situation changes completely if we consider infinitely many *pairs of stockings* instead of pairs of shoes. The difference lies in the fact that manufacturers produce identical stockings for both feet. Certainly, we may start by assigning to the first pair an *arbitrary* stocking of this pair and to the second pair the other stocking of the first pair. Then an arbitrary stocking of the second pair will correspond to the third pair, the other to the fourth, etc. Yet now we can continue this procedure only finitely many times, unless we are prepared to admit an infinity of arbitrary choices of stockings out of the pairs of stockings. So long as we exclude this, in accordance with mathematical tradition throughout history, we cannot determine whether the set of all stockings has the same cardinal $\aleph_0$ as the set of all pairs.

Of course, the significance this example is merely expositional, not scientific. But we have already given an example in which an important problem seems to be unsolvable without the use of an infinity of choices: the definition of finiteness (of a set, hence of a number) and, more specifically, the logical equivalence between the concepts of inductive and nonreflexive sets. Thus there emerges *a new principle of logic and mathematics, which was discovered only at the beginning of the twentieth century*, and which is indispensable for proving many important statements in various branches of modern mathematics. This principle is called the *axiom of choice* (after

Zermelo, who first introduced it in 1904), or the *multiplicative principle* (after Russell, who found a better formulation in 1906).

We shall devote the remainder of this section to a short survey of topics relating to the axiom of choice: its formulation and early history, its logical nature, and its application in mathematics.

When proving Theorem 1 on p. 27, we chose infinitely many elements i_n *in succession,* where each choice was dependent on the preceding choices. This is rather awkward, since the time factor seems to be relevant. A preferable procedure would be to make all choices *simultaneously* and independently of each other, as follows.

We postulate that *an arbitrary fixed element i of $\bar{I}$ is assigned* to every nonempty subset $\bar{I}$ of the noninductive set I (Theorem 1). We call i the *distinguished element* of the subset $\bar{I}$ and write $i = f(\bar{I})$, where f is the corresponding "choice function." Of course, this postulate goes further than necessary. It provides far more choices than are required for the proof of Theorem 1 — in fact it follows from Cantor's theorem (Section 5) that it involves $\aleph$ choices instead of only $\aleph_0$. This, then, is the price paid for replacing successive choices by simultaneous ones, and contemporary scientific taste considers this price to be not unreasonable. In the above proof of Theorem 1, our postulate would be used to produce the elements i_{n+1} as the distinguished elements $f(I_n)$ of the remainders I_n, which are nonempty (even noninductive, i.e., infinite).

In this formulation of our postulate, which refers to subsets of a set, the distinguished elements of different subsets need not be different. On the contrary, we may take the first step in producing a choice function by selecting an arbitrary element and stipulating that it shall be the distinguished element of *any* subset to which it belongs. This step, comprehensive as it may seem, is nevertheless far from being a conclusive contribution to the establishment of a choice function. As will be seen later (in fact in Section 7), a choice function cannot be established in a constructive manner.

Disregarding the particular case of Theorem 1, we may now express our postulate in the following general form.

GENERAL AXIOM OF CHOICE (Zermelo, 1908). To any set S, the elements of which are nonempty sets, there corresponds at least one univalent function $f(x)$ such that for every element x of S, $f(x)$ is an element of the set x. In such a case, f is called a *choice function.*

If s, s', $\cdots$ are elements of S, this principle asserts the existence of a function f such that $f(s)$ belongs to s, $f(s')$ to s', etc. Except for the trivial case when each element of S is a set with only a single element (in which case the axiom of choice is not needed to produce f), there clearly exist various choice functions for a given set S. In fact, if σ_1 and σ_2 are different elements of a certain s that belongs to S, and if $f(s)=\sigma_1$ by the choice function f, then any function f^* for which $f^*(s)=\sigma_2$ is another choice function.

The above formulation of the axiom of choice involves both psychological difficulties and technical complications.

The latter derive partly from the fact that different values of the arguments x may produce the same value of $f(x)$. It also seems rather far-fetched to introduce the concept of *function* into a set-theoretical principle, though, in fact, the concept of function can be reduced to that of set, and conversely. Psychologically, it is awkward to imagine that certain arbitrary elements $f(x)$ are "selected" or "chosen" by the function f from each single element x of S. Therefore the name given to this principle by Zermelo is rather unfortunate (although now universally accepted).

For these reasons it is preferable to formulate the principle in the more special "multiplicative" form due to Russell (1906):

AXIOM OF CHOICE. If S is a *disjoint* set of nonempty sets, i.e., such that any two members of S have no common element, then *there exists* at least one set C which contains a single element out of each element of S.

Any such set C is called a *choice set* of S. If $S=\{s,\ s',\ \cdots\ \}$, then every choice set of S has the form $\{\sigma,\ \sigma',\ \cdots\}$, where σ belongs to s, σ' to s' etc., and they are distinct since the set S is disjoint. By means of this formulation we have eliminated the function concept and arbitrary "choices" and the problem has been reduced to the existence of sets. The axioms of set theory alone should determine what sets do actually exist.

As shown by Zermelo (1908), the general axiom of choice can be derived from the above axiom by constructive procedures which are generally recognized in logic and mathematics.

A further understanding of the nature and the purpose of the axiom of choice is obtained by the following argument, which shows why Russell (rightly) favored the name "multiplicative axiom." This argument will also enable the reader to judge to what extent the statement of the axiom of choice may be regarded as reasonable, or even evident.

Our aim is to generalize the elementary theorem of arithmetic that a product of two or more integers is zero *if and only if a factor is zero*. The product of positive integers (finite cardinals), for instance $3 \cdot 4$, may be introduced into set theory as follows.

We form two arbitrary disjoint sets of 3 and 4 elements respectively, say $s = \{a_1, a_2, a_3\}$ and $s' = \{b_1, b_2, b_3, b_4\}$; the disjointness means that s and s' have no common members. From these sets we form their *Cartesian product*, i.e., the set $s \times s'$ whose elements are all pairs, consisting of a single element of s and a single element of s'. In the present case, then, the Cartesian product is the set

$$s \times s' = \{\{a_1, b_1\}, \{a_1, b_2\}, \{a_1, b_3\}, \{a_1, b_4\}, \{a_2, b_1\}, \{a_2, b_2\}, \{a_2, b_3\}, \{a_2, b_4\}, \}a_3, b_1\},$$

$$\{a_3, b_2\}, \{a_3, b_3\}, \{a_3, b_4\}\},$$

which contains $3 \cdot 4 = 12$ elements. In the same way any product of positive integers can be represented as the cardinal number of a corresponding Cartesian product, and the factor 0 can be included as the cardinal of the empty set (null set). In fact, a Cartesian product, one of whose factors is the null set, itself equals the null set because there exists *no* pair with an element from the null set.

This train of thought can be extended without change to include *infinite sets* as factors of a Cartesian product, and even *infinitely many* factors $s, s', s'', \cdots$. Instead of pairs we then obtain "complexes" $\{\sigma, \sigma', \sigma'', \cdots\}$, i.e., sets which contain a single element out of each factor of the product. The product of (finitely or infinitely many) cardinals will then be defined as the cardinal of the corresponding Cartesian product.[6]

After this generalization it remains clear that if the empty set is one of the factors, the Cartesian product is itself empty, hence its cardinal is 0. The converse question is less simple. For the sake of simplicity we shall again assume that any two factors are disjoint. It seems natural to reason as follows: If the factors $s, s', s'', \cdots$ are nonempty sets, then we may choose a single element $\sigma, \sigma', \sigma'', \cdots$, respectively, out of each factor. However they are chosen, these elements are distinct because the factors are disjoint. Therefore the set of all chosen elements, $\{\sigma, \sigma', \sigma'', \cdots\}$, is an element of the Cartesian product $s \times s' \times s'' \times \cdots$, which shows that this product is not empty; hence its cardinal differs from 0. The logical converse of this result states that a Cartesian product can be empty *only* if at least one factor is empty.

But in reaching this result we have used the above axiom of choice, by choosing arbitrary elements out of each factor $s, s', s'', \cdots$. Thus the nonemptiness of a product of non-empty disjoint factors is based on the axiom of choice in Russell's formulation, and essentially even *coincides* with this axiom; hence Russell's expression "multiplicative axiom."

This train of thought may be expressed in a still more striking way that emphasizes the contrast with traditional methods in logic and mathematics. The elements of any choice set of S (p. 34) belong to elements of S; therefore a choice set is *a certain subset of the union U* (p. 6) *of the elements of S*. In general, a subset is defined by a property which is characteristic of the elements of the subset. For instance, from the set N of all positive integers we obtain, through the property "even," the subset of all even positive integers, a subset which is uniquely determined by N and by the property. Yet in the present case the situation is different. The characteristic property of the choice sets, regarded as subsets of the union U, is that they have a *single common element with each element of S*. Clearly, in general it is *not a single subset* of the union U that is determined by this property; various subsets—usually infinitely many—have the property (cf. p.34). Thus the existence of a choice set cannot, in general, be guaranteed in a constructive way. It is a purely existential statement.

---

6 See (for two factors) Cantor (1932), p. 286 (appeared in 1895).

In the case of the infinite set S of pairs of stockings, the union U is the set of all stockings contained in the pairs; a choice set of S is any subset of U which contains a single stocking out of each pair. If a choice set exists, then infinitely many others also exist, namely, those formed by replacing a given stocking by the other stocking of the same pair, in one or several pairs.

The history of the axiom of choice is interesting and may in some respects be compared with the most famous axiom in mathematics, Euclid's parallel axiom. In the 1880's and 1890's Cantor had already in some proofs used an argument which is logically equivalent to our axiom, yet he had done so implicitly and was not conscious of using a new principle. In 1902 Beppo Levi, in considering the proof of a certain theorem of set theory, explicitly referred to the statement of the axiom. In 1904 the axiom appeared as the basis of Zermelo's (first) proof of the well-ordering theorem (see Section 7), which stands out among the achievements of modern mathematics both with respect to its far-reaching consequences and the various critical attitudes that it provoked. Between 1904 and 1910, papers which took exception to Zermelo's proof, mostly by rejecting the axiom of choice, were published in many leading mathematical journals. In particular, a few prominent French mathematicians expressed a negative opinion. On the other hand, the leading French scholar of that time [Poincaré (1910)] remarked: "...and this seems to be the reason for the dispute about Zermelo's ingenious theorem. This dispute is rather strange: one side rejects the axiom of choice but accepts the proof; the other accepts the axiom but not the proof of the theorem." (Poincaré himself belonged to the "other," who were and are a small minority.)

In 1908 Zermelo proved the well-ordering theorem by a fundamentally different method which is of a logical rather than a mathematical nature, but which also depends on the axiom of choice. Even then the discussion of the axiom did not abate, and essentially the differences are no less radical today than half a century ago. An important (rather pragmatical) argument was formulated by E. Steinitz in the introduction to his comprehensive paper [Steinitz (1910)] in which he laid the foundations of abstract algebra, namely : "Many mathematicians still take a negative attitude towards the axiom of choice. Yet the clearer it becomes that *there are mathematical problems which cannot be settled without the use of this axiom*, the more the opposition is bound to weaken. On the other hand, for methodological reasons, it is desirable to avoid the axiom, as long as the nature of the problems does not render its use imperative." Steinitz' prediction that the opposition would gradually weaken has not, however, come true.

Many objections against the axiom of choice are based on misunderstandings and are therefore void, inasmuch as they ignore the *purely existential nature* of its statement. Because of this existentiality it is quite natural and to be expected that one cannot deduce from the well-ordering theorem *where* in the series of cardinals the cardinal $\aleph$ of the continuum (p. 25) is to be found. This question constitutes the *continuum problem*; to solve it, we need a constructive formation of the corresponding choice set. As a matter of fact, except for a partial (though profound) result of Gödel in 1938–40, the attempts made by outstanding mathematicians since the early 1880's to solve this problem remained unsuccessful until 1963. It is psychologically understandable that the mistrust toward the axiom of choice has deepened, because it is of no help in the solution of the continuum problem. In 1963 Paul J. Cohen showed in an ingenious proof that the problem is *unsolvable*; that is to say, various positions in the series of alephs for the cardinal of the continuum are compatible with the axioms of set theory.

Yet only those mathematicians and philosophers who in principle acknowledge only constructive, not existential, procedures are entitled to reject the axiom of choice for such reasons; among these, in particular, are the so-called intuitionistic and neo-intuitionistic schools. However, insofar as they keep to their principles, they are bound to restrict the methods of mathematics to such an extent that, outside of arithmetic, only narrow fields can be investigated.

Actually, psychological rather than logical reasons played a leading part in the rejection of the axiom of choice. Prominent among them was the aversion to the well-ordering theorem, which was considered too strong a statement that yielded too few "practical" results. On the other hand, most critics had to admit that if the axiom of choice were accepted they could discover no shortcoming in Zermelo's proofs (cf. Section 7). Hence the only way out seemed to be the rejection of the axiom of choice. Poincaré, who would not adopt this attitude, criticized instead a supposed use of an "impredicative" procedure in the proof. But this objection, convincingly refuted by Zermelo, did not meet with approval in other circles.

A philosophical ingredient which lacks a properly mathematical foundation has essentially, though mainly subconsciously, influenced these discussions. It is the question, *do we discover or invent mathematical concepts*? Anyone who accepts the (Platonic) doctrine of the pre-existence of these concepts will naturally see no reason why, among the subsets of the union of all elements of S (p. 35), just those subsets that are distinguished by having a single common element with each element of S should be absent. Hence, if they are not absent, we just "discover" them by stating this distinguishing property. However, if the existence of a concept means the possibility of "inventing" or constructing it, then the existence of choice sets remains doubtful so long as we lack a procedure for constructing such sets, even though a considerable part of mathematics becomes questionable without them. The outstanding logician F.P. Ramsey (deceased at 27) used the attitude of "discovering" in attacking the conception of *Principia Mathematica*,[7] where the axiom of choice does not appear among the (logical) axioms but is introduced as a specific hypothesis which is mentioned at the beginning of the proof of any theorem depending on it.

It is a strange phenomenon, which rarely occurs in the exact sciences, that discussions become stagnant over a period of many decades. Yet this is what happened to the axiom of choice, and hardly any fundamentally new ideas have emerged in the discussions. In 1938 —34 years after the formulation of the axiom—Lebesgue, one of the leading mathematicians of the last generation, modified his earlier opposition to the axiom of choice by declaring[8] *"En énonçant ainsi mes exigences, je n'ai nullement voulu décider en faveur de la position purement négative que j'ai adoptée. Je ne la regarde nullement comme définitive; ce n'est qu'une position d'attente; je l'ai qualifiée de position de prudence et même peut-être de routine, il y a de bien longues années déjà, dès les premiers jours de la controverse."*

This exciting development, and even more the fact that the axiom of choice is indispensable in most domains of mathematics (cf. below), raises two questions:

1. Is the axiom *independent* of the classical principles of logic and mathematics, or can it *be proved* by their means?

2. Is the axiom *compatible* with those principles, or can its addition yield a *contradiction*? (In spite of certain connections between these questions, they are essentially different.)

---

7 Whitehead-Russell(1910–13); cf. Ramsey (1926). True, there exist certain paradoxical consequences of the axiom of choice, for instance Hausdorff's discovery that half of a sphere's surface is congruent to a third of it [Hausdorff (1914), p. 469]. Yet far stranger consequences follow from the negation of the axiom.

8 Lebesgue (1941), p. 118. This declaration appeared in the report of an international colloquium on the foundations of mathematics, held in Zurich in 1938.

Surprisingly, the first question was not solved in its entirety until 1963. Since 1922, and in a more profound sense since 1938, the independence of the axiom of choice has been proved under various conditions.[9] However, all these proofs use an *ad hoc* assumption, which is unnecessary from the general point of view (or else an assumption which is only formally weaker),[10] namely, that in the set-theoretical domain under consideration there exist infinitely many "individuals," i.e., objects which are not sets. Without such assumptions no one had succeeded in proving the independence of the axiom. Yet in 1963, Paul J. Cohen, in the proof mentioned above, was able to show without any assumption that the axiom of choice is indeed independent.

On the other hand, the fact that the axiom of choice is compatible with the other principles of set theory was proved by Gödel in several profound papers from 1938 on [see especially Gödel (1940)]. The same papers also deal with the continuum problem (cf. p. 37). Comparing Gödel's result with the situation described in the preceding paragraph, we see that the remaining desideratum was either a proof that the *negation* of the choice axiom is also compatible, or a proof that the negation is contradictory. Now that the former proof has been given by P. Cohen, we find ourselves in a situation somewhat similar to that which has existed in geometry since the middle of the 19th century with respect to the axiom of parallels. There, besides Euclidean geometry and the non-Euclidean (hyperbolic) geometry that results from negating the parallel axiom, we have absolute geometry, which deals with the propositions that hold true independently of the validity or invalidity of the axiom of parallels. The analogue of absolute geometry in the present case is that part of set theory which can be treated without reference to the axiom of choice. [This analogy is intended from a purely mathematical point of view; philosophically it may become dubious, especially for Platonists (cf. Gödel, 1947).]

Finally, we shall outline *the significance and the applications of the axiom of choice in various branches of mathematics.* The axiom is used throughout analysis, especially in the theory of real functions, as well as in set theory and in wide domains of topology. As far as set theory is concerned, the

---

9 See Fraenkel (1922), Lindenbaum-Mostowski (1938), Mostowski (1939), and the account of the problems connected with the axiom of choice in Fraenkel and Bar-Hillel (1958), pp. 44–80.

10 The existence of so-called extraordinary sets, the possibilty of which was first pointed out in Mirimanoff (1917).

arithmetic of transfinite cardinals, ordinals, and order types (see Sections 6 and 7) is essentially based upon the choice axiom.[11] Its indispensability in abstract algebra was mentioned on p. 36, although in this field it has been customary since the 1930's to use a maximum principle (for instance, that of Zorn) which is equivalent to the axiom of choice, but more adapted to algebraic purposes.

It should be stressed again that the axiom of choice is needed for a full analysis of *the concepts of finite set and finite number* (*cardinal, ordinal*). One can prove without the axiom that an inductive set cannot be reflexive (equivalent to a proper subset of itself, see p. 28), and by logical inversion we infer that a reflexive set is not inductive. Yet the only specific conclusion that results from this is a classification of sets—and hence, by passing to their cardinals, of numbers—into three classes: the *finite*, more specifically the inductive, sets and numbers $(0, 1, 2, \cdots)$; the *infinite*, more specifically the reflexive, sets and cardinals ($\aleph_0$, etc.); and finally, the sets which are neither inductive nor reflexive, and their cardinals, occasionally called "mediate." Only by using the axiom of choice can we prove that *mediate sets and cardinals do not exist*, hence that any set or cardinal is either finite or infinite. This is done by means of Theorem 1 on p. 26, according to which any noninductive set has a denumerable subset and therefore is reflexive. Hence any noninductive cardinal either equals $\aleph_0$ or is greater than $\aleph_0$ (cf. p. 41).

Thus although the axiom of choice has entered science only recently, it has proved indispensable for the structure and development of mathematics.

---

[11] A comprehensive account of the consequences of the axiom in the *arithmetic of cardinals* is contained in section V of the concise but comprehensive book by Bachmann (1955). An exhaustive survey of equivalents of the axiom of choice is found in Rubin-Rubin (1963).

Section 5. Transfinite Cardinals. Paradoxes of Set Theory and Attempts at their Elimination

In Section 3 we became acquainted with two different transfinite cardinals: the cardinal $\aleph_0$ of the denumerable sets and the cardinal $\aleph$ of the continuum. Although from the first it seemed natural to consider $\aleph_0$ "smaller" than $\aleph$, we still lack a rigorous definition of ordering cardinals "according to magnitude." For this purpose we may start from the order of *finite numbers*, which can be expressed as follows: the cardinal (i.e., the number of elements) of the set F_1 is smaller than the cardinal of F_2 if F_1 is a proper subset of F_2 or, more generally, if F_1 is equivalent to a proper subset of F_2.

Clearly, this definition cannot be applied to the infinite domain since any infinite set is equivalent to a proper subset of itself; hence the definition would imply that a transfinite cardinal is smaller than itself. Yet the following modification will prove adequate for ordering both finite and transfinite cardinals.

DEFINITION OF ORDERING FOR CARDINALS. The cardinal of the set S is *smaller than* ($<$) the cardinal of T if S is equivalent to a subset of T but T is not equivalent to any subset of S. Conversely, the cardinal of T is then called *greater than* ($>$) the cardinal of S.

It is easy to confirm that this definition, in which the stress on proper subsets is clearly unnecessary, is in accordance with the usual ordering of the finite numbers (positive integers) according to their magnitude. It also follows that any finite cardinal is smaller than any transfinite cardinal. The truth of the relation $\aleph_0 < \aleph$ is shown if we take S to be the set of the positive integers and T to be a continuum, e.g., the set of all real numbers: S is a subset of T, while according to p. 13 any subset of S is finite or denumerable, and therefore not equivalent to T; hence $\aleph_0 < \aleph$.

Even from the viewpoint of ordinary arithmetic, the domain of transfinite cardinals would be extremely poor if it contained no more than the

41

two cardinals, $\aleph_0$ and $\aleph$. A surprising step forward is contained in the following far-reaching theorem.

CANTOR'S THEOREM.[1] *Given any finite or transfinite cardinal, there exists a greater one. More precisely, if S is any set, then the set CS whose elements are all the subsets of S has a greater cardinal than S. Hence, besides the finite cardinals, there exist infinitely many transfinite cardinals.*

For reasons to be explained later (pp. 44 and 64), *CS* is called the *power set of S*.

The following proof, although it requires almost no mathematical technique, may cause beginners some difficulty. Nevertheless, readers are strongly advised to work through the proof, which has fundamental logical consequences in various directions.

We shall prove that *S is equivalent to a subset of CS, but that it is not equivalent to CS itself.* The additional part of the proof, namely, that *CS* is not equivalent to any *subset* of *S*, is quite easy (cf. p. 65) and without major significance.

The first statement, viz., that *S* is equivalent to a subset of *CS*, is almost evident. For any element *s* of *S* we may form the unit set $\{s\}$ which is a subset of *S*; hence the set *U* of all unit sets $\{s\}$ is a subset of *CS*, and naturally a proper subset. Finally, *U* is shown to be equivalent to *S* by the mapping which assigns the element *s* of *S* to the element $\{s\}$ of *CS*.

Our essential task, therefore, is to prove the second statement, viz., that $S \sim CS$ is impossible. We shall prove this indirectly. Logically, though not psychologically, the direct proof would be practically the same.

We start from the hypothesis, to be refuted in the end, that a mapping of *S* onto *CS* does exist. Let φ be such a fixed mapping, and let us denote by $\varphi(s)$ that element of *CS* that is assigned by φ to the element *s* of *S*; as an element of *CS*, $\varphi(s)$ is a subset of *S*. We now distinguish between two cases: first, that *s* is an element of the set $\varphi(s)$; second, that *s* does not

---

[1] The essence of the proof is contained in a paper of 1892 which is reprinted in Cantor (1932), pp. 278–80. For a more complete proof see Hessenberg (1906), p. 41.

To be sure, Cantor had proved much earlier that there exist infinitely many transfinite cardinals of a special kind. That proof, however, is far more complicated and uses ordered sets; cf. Section 7.

belong to $\varphi(s)$. Accordingly, the element s of S will be referred to as of *the first or second kind*, respectively.[2]

In order to refute our hypothesis, we investigate the set S^* *which contains all elements of the second kind*. Since S^* is a subset of S, S^* is an element of CS, and by our hypothesis there exists an element s^* of S such that $S^* = \varphi(s^*)$. But this leads to a contradiction. For s^* is either of the first or of the second kind. In the first case, s^* is an element of $\varphi(s^*) = S^*$, which is impossible, since S^*, according to its definition, contains only elements of the second kind. On the other hand, s^* being of the second kind means that s^* does *not* belong to $\varphi(s^*) = S^*$, which contradicts the definition of S^* as the set of *all* elements of the second kind. Hence our hypothesis is untenable; S is not equivalent to CS, but only to a subset of CS.

Readers should not feel discouraged by the apparently paradoxical nature of our proof. The contradiction we have obtained shows that the power set of S is *too comprehensive* to allow it to be mapped onto S; that was the aim of the proof. Later we shall proceed from this *apparent* paradox to an *actual* one.

We conclude with a few remarks on the method of our proof and on the consequences of Cantor's theorem. A thorough analysis of the proof will convince the reader that here again, as on p. 21, we have used the diagonal method; the set S^* corresponds to the decimal d constructed in the former proof. More precisely, the proof of the nondenumerability of the continuum may be regarded as a *particular case* of the present proof. In fact, one may consider the set of all real numbers to be the power set of the denumerable set of all rational numbers, since a real number may be regarded as a certain denumerable set (or sequence) of rationals.

Cantor's theorem also holds, of course, for finite sets and cardinals; in our proof we did not assume that S was infinite. Starting with the null set $\emptyset$, we obtain the simplest cases of Cantor's theorem as follows:

$$C\,\emptyset = \{\emptyset\}^3, \, C\,\{\emptyset\} = \{\emptyset, \{\emptyset\}\}, \, C\,\{\emptyset, \{\emptyset\}\} = \{\emptyset, \{\emptyset\}, \{\{\emptyset\}\}, \{\emptyset, \{\emptyset\}\}\}, \cdots$$

---

[2] It is irrelevant for our proof whether there exist members of both kinds. In fact they do exist: in view of the mapping φ the s for which $\varphi(s) = S$ is of the first kind, and the s for which $\varphi(s)$ is the null set is of the second kind. (The null set, being a subset of S, is a member of CS.)

[3] Since the null set has no subset besides itself, its power set is the set whose only element is the null set—while the null set has no element at all.

Passing from these equalities between *sets* to the corresponding *cardinals*, we see that Cantor's theorem in the finite case merely expresses the well-known inequalities

$$0 < 1 \;(= 2^0), \; 1 < 2 \;(= 2^1), \; 2 < 4 \;(= 2^2),$$

and so, in general, $n < 2^n$. In fact, a finite set F of n members has exactly 2^n subsets, including the null set and F itself; this is an elementary combinatorial theorem (cf. p. 56). Therefore, the name "power set" is quite natural in this case.

Applying Cantor's theorem to infinite sets, we obtain a far-reaching generalization of the inequality $\aleph_0 < \aleph$ (see p. 64). To formulate the generalization easily, we now write k_0 for $\aleph_0$ (i.e., the least transfinite cardinal, namely, the cardinal of denumerable sets), k_1 for the cardinal $\aleph$ of the continuum (i.e., of the power set of a denumerable set), and in general, k_{n+1} for the cardinal of the power set of a set having the cardinal k_n. Cantor's theorem then gives the infinite sequence of inequalities

$$k_0 < k_1 < k_2 < \cdots < k_n < k_{n+1} < \cdots,$$

the first of which coincides with $\aleph_0 < \aleph$. Thus the strength of our theorem becomes obvious.

Attentive readers may ask why we have used a new symbol k after having introduced the symbol $\aleph$, with various indices, for the transfinite cardinals (p. 25). This question indeed touches a tender point already hinted at on p. 25. The symbols $\aleph_0, \aleph_1, \aleph_2, \cdots, \aleph_n, \aleph_{n+1}, \cdots$ are defined by the rule that $\aleph_0$ is the least transfinite cardinal and $\aleph_{n+1}$ follows $\aleph_n$ as the next-greater cardinal. (In fact, it can be shown by a rather profound method that a single next-greater cardinal always exists.) However, in view of the above definition of k_n through the power set it was not known whether k_{n+1} is next to k_n (as 2^1 is next to 2^0) or not (as 2^{n+1} is not next to 2^n for positive integers n). In particular, it was not known whether other cardinals intervene between $k_0 (= \aleph_0)$ and $k_1 (= \aleph)$. The latter question, called *Cantor's continuum problem*, had been raised by Cantor about 1880. The corresponding question regarding any k_n (or any $\aleph_n$) is called *the generalized continuum problem*. There are stricter formulations of both problems.

As early as 1900, at the International Congress of Mathematicians in Paris, Hilbert, who, together with Poincaré, was a leading mathematician of his generation, had started his list of important unsolved mathematical problems with the continuum problem. During 80 years, outstanding mathematicians, including Hilbert, have shown much ingenuity in attempts to solve the problem, but in vain. Only in 1938 did Gödel obtain an important partial result. He showed that the *continuum hypothesis*, which affirms that $\aleph$ is next to $\aleph_0$ and, in general, that k_{n+1} is next to k_n, is *compatible* (noncontradictory) in a well-defined sense.[4] Clearly, this is no more a *proof* of the hypothesis than the noncontradictory nature of Euclidean geometry is a proof of Euclid's parallel axiom (which would mean a refutation of non-Euclidean geometry). In fact, in the case of geometry, the parallel axiom is *independent* of the other axioms and accordingly *unprovable*. As Paul Cohen showed in 1963, the resources of current mathematics are not sufficient to decide the continuum problem; the hypothesis $2^{\aleph_0} = \aleph_1$ (p. 64) and its generalization are *independent* of the axioms of contemporary mathematics.

The above sequence of inequalities shows that the domain of transfinite cardinals is at least as comprehensive as the domain of finite numbers, i.e., of integers. Actually it is far more comprehensive, for according to the method described on p. 58 we may form the union of infinitely many mutually disjoint sets of cardinals $k_0, k_1, \cdots, k_n, \cdots$, respectively, for all integers n. This union has a cardinal s greater than any k_n. For, if n denotes any particular positive integer, then $k_n < s$, because the union certainly has subsets of cardinals greater than k_n; for instance, a subset of the cardinal k_{n+1}. Hence there exist greater transfinite cardinals than those contained in the sequence $(k_1, k_2, \cdots)$, even infinitely many greater ones.

This enormous comprehensiveness is due to the possibility of forming sums with infinitely many terms, to an extent which greatly surpasses the sum formed above (see Section 6). (The summation of infinite convergent series as defined in analysis has nothing to do with the present sums, which are of a purely arithmetical nature and do not depend on limit and convergence.)

So far, this section has provided us with interesting results which seem to confirm Hilbert's dictum about the "paradise" created by Cantor, to be regarded as "the most admirable blossom of mathematical thought, and altogether even one of the supreme achievements of human intellectual activity."[5] Unfortunately, however, we shall now see that some of the results of set theory, in particular Cantor's theorem and its proof, bring us close to a gulf which is difficult to bridge. The matter is serious enough to have induced important mathematicians to speak of Cantor's

[4] See Gödel (1940).
[5] Hilbert (1925), p. 167.

work as a "pathological entanglement" which later generations would look upon with bewilderment.

To describe the situation we start from the proof of Cantor's theorem given above and construct an apparently quite similar argument which will involve us in a contradiction. According to Aristotle's Principle of the Excluded Middle (*tertium non datur*), given any set S, there exists the alternative that either S is an element of S, or it is not.[6] For brevity, we shall call sets of the second kind "normal sets." We now consider the set Ω which contains as its elements *all normal sets and only those sets*.

The set Ω is either of the first or of the second (normal) kind. In the former case we have that Ω is an element of Ω, i.e., that Ω is not normal. But this contradicts the definition of Ω by which Ω contains normal sets only. Apparently we have thus proved that Ω is a normal set. But then Ω, containing all normal sets, must also contain the element Ω, which means that Ω is *not* normal. Hence the second assumption is contradictory too, and so Ω, being neither of the first nor the second kind, cannot exist, although it has been defined in an apparently legitimate way and certainly in accordance with Cantor's definition of set (p. 4).

The argument used here is completely analogous to our proof of Cantor's theorem. The only difference is that in the proof of Cantor's theorem the contradiction arises from the *assumption* that a set is equivalent to its power set, an assumption which is refuted by the contradiction. In the present argument, however, no assumption has been made. Thus, it seems as though the very concept of set leads to a contradiction. This contradiction has become famous as the *Russell paradox* (1902); at the same time it had been discovered independently by Zermelo.

Russell also gave a kind of "translation" of his paradox from mathematical to logical language, in order to show that the contradiction is of a logical nature and does not originate from mathematical technique (concept of set). We call a concept "predicable" if it can be predicated of itself; otherwise the concept is "impredicable." For instance, "abstract"

----

6 As in the previous proof, it is irrelevant whether or not sets of both kinds do exist. The "ordinary" sets certainly are normal sets; the simplest example is the null set, which does not contain itself because it contains no element. Any set of, say, geometrical objects is also normal. On the other hand, the set which contains *all* sets as its elements may be cited as a set which is not normal.

is predicable, "concrete" (or "green") is impredicable. We examine the concept "impredicable." Assume it to be predicable; thus, the statement " 'impredicable' is impredicable" is true, contrary to the assumption. Hence it must be impredicable, i.e., the statement " 'impredicable' is impredicable" is false, which means that "impredicable" is predicable. Thus either assumption leads to a contradiction.

We now mention a similar paradox which is not connected with the *proof* of Cantor's theorem but with its very *assertion*. Let Z be the set which contains *all sets* as its elements. The set Z, then, is the most comprehensive of all conceivable sets of sets. On the other hand, the set CZ, whose elements are all subsets of Z, is also a set of sets, and CZ is not only more comprehensive than Z but even has a greater cardinal, according to Cantor's theorem!

In Section 7 we shall give another paradox of a strictly mathematical nature (p. 84).

When such logical paradoxes appeared at the turn of the century they caused consternation among logicians and mathematicians, who saw their methods—including the logical foundation of arithmetic by Dedekind and Frege—shaken and the results becoming dubious. Yet the initial shock was not deepened, but mitigated, when Russell developed systematic procedures for obtaining entire classes of similar paradoxes.[7] We shall later discuss another type of paradox (not purely logical), which emerged at the same time.

We cannot describe here the numerous attempts to eliminate or "solve" the paradoxes by narrowing the scope of mathematics or by restricting the logical methods which are admissible. During the past sixty years, hundreds of papers and books have been devoted to this aim, yet the results are shockingly meager by comparison with the efforts that have been made. Later we shall discuss in detail the axiomatic method, which has proved particularly useful here, but first we shall outline two other approaches which have also attracted considerable attention.

One approach is connected with a profound *reform of logic*, initiated by Russell through his Theory of Types [see Russell (1908)].[8] The original "ramified" theory has few adherents today, partly because it is very com-

---

[7] Notably in Russell (1903).

[8] Recently a foundation of set theory has been given which combines the theory of types with the axiomatic method : Klaua (1964).

plicated and partly because it is hardly workable without the introduction of an *ad hoc* axiom, namely, Russell's axiom of reducibility, which is far from being evident or even plausible. Yet the "simple" theory of types still attracts interest among large circles of logicians because it is logically sound to such an extent that in retrospect it is difficult to understand why it was not formulated much earlier. We may regard Russell's *vicious circle principle* (cf. p. 54) as the starting point of the theory of types. It excludes "impredicative" totalities, that is to say, totalities which contain elements that are definable only by reference to the totality itself. (For instance, the set Ω introduced on p. 46, and possibly also the sets Z and CZ, violate the principle.)

However, even the simple theory of types is not very popular with mathematicians because it involves complications and discriminations that present great difficulties even in simple problems. It is true that various ingenious devices have been introduced to meet these difficulties, but the situation still remains far from satisfactory.

A diametrically opposed direction is taken by neo-intuitionism[9] as introduced and developed since 1907 by Brouwer and his school.[10] Here logic is not being reformed but completely abolished. The fundamental neo-intuitionistic postulate entails restriction to *constructive* procedures, since the essence of mathematics is supposedly construction. This involves the abolition of the traditional principle of the excluded middle (*tertium non datur*) or, more exactly, the rejection of the principle by which negating a general statement (of the form "all *a*'s are *b*") means affirming an existential statement ("there is an *a* which is *non-b*"). Brouwer asserts that the *tertium non datur*, the third principle of Aristotelian logic,[11] originates from an unjustified generalization of a proposition which is valid in the domain of *finite* sets only. (It is true that in this domain the alternative "either all *a*'s are *b*, or else at least one *a* is *non-b*" can be reached in a constructive way, by enumerating the *a*'s and examining each one.) Moreover, he maintains

---

9 The qualification "neo" was added by Brouwer to distinguish his attitude from the earlier "semi-intuitionistic" systems of various French mathematicians, which are less radical.

10 See Brouwer (1907) and (1912). Recently, systematic expositions were given in Heyting (1956) and Fraenkel-Bar Hillel (1958), Chapter IV. In view of the geographical origin of Brouwer, Heyting, van Dantzig, Belinfante, and other neo-intuitionists, one also speaks of the Dutch School. A more profound monograph is Kleene-Vesley (1964).

11 These intuitionistic groups which admit negation as a logical operation maintain the second principle of "contradiction" but there are also *negationless* groups.

that this alternative in finite domains is typical of the (empirical) character of logic which arises by *a posteriori* abstractions from constructive mathematical procedures. Furthermore, the secondary role which is assigned to logic is in full agreement with the neo-intuitionistic assessment of *language*, contrary to the opinion of leading philosophers of the past and the present. The Dutch school considers language not to be a primary ingredient of human thought but only an expedient for transmitting abstract constructions from one human being to another. Therefore language will always be inexact and subject to error, no matter whether historical languages or symbolic ones are concerned.

It is not surprising that these attitudes imply far-reaching liimtations, not only of the methods, but also of the very domain of mathematics. In fact, most of the achievements in analysis, geometry and set theory during the last three centuries, including even certain parts of arithmetic and algebra, are rejected by neo-intuitionism, being declared "false" or "meaningless."

Most mathematicians are inclined to look for more conservative ways of avoiding the paradoxes, preferably by an axiomatization of set theory, logic and other branches of mathematics. We cannot give here a detailed account of the *axiomatic method*, which originated with Euclid's Elements and won a new start in the 19th century as a result of the researches on non-Euclidean geometry. Since the turn of the century, axiomatics has expanded enormously and has attained methodological depth, primarily at the hands of Hilbert[12] and his direct and indirect pupils, who emphasized the need for laying more solid foundations and stressed the importance of independence and compatibility proofs.

Briefly, but not exhaustively, one may characterize the axiomatic method as the process of *collecting those primary concepts and statements* of a certain branch of science from which all its concepts and statements can be deductively derived by means of definitions and proofs. The primary concepts and statements—the latter called *axioms*—do not require, or even admit, definitions or proofs. The reference to deduction,[13] which is already predominant

---

12 For the first stage of this development see Hilbert (1918); cf. Weyl (1949).

13 The importance of the *deductive method* for philosophical research explains why Plato, in the alleged inscription over the entrance to his 'Academy,' debarred students ignorant of geometry. (The methods of geometry used by Middle Eastern peoples in Mesopotamia and Egypt were inductive; in modern times the methods of natural science have remained, and will remain, fundamentally inductive, no matter the extent to which deductive [mathematical] ingredients enter scientific research.) A leading mathematician of our generation, asked to define *what is mathematics*, answered: mathematics deals with the logical deductions from assumed premises.

in Euclid's axiomatic system of geometry, implies that, strictly speaking, an axiomatized system is not determined if the corresponding logic has not been specified. Moreover, since in an axiomatic system the primary concepts, and hence also the axioms containing these concepts, have no material meaning, the system has a *purely formal* nature. Therefore one ought to show that the system is noncontradictory, either by an abstract logical proof or by producing a *model* that contains concepts which correspond to the primary concepts of the system and which are connected by relations corresponding to the relations that appear in the axioms.

In the various branches of *arithmetic* and *analysis*, we have at our disposal not only the axiomatic method, but also the genetic (definitory, constructive) method, provided that the system of positive integers is either based on special axioms, as proposed by Peano, or reduced to logical concepts, as in the approach of Frege, Dedekind, and Russell. A different situation arises in *geometry*, however, where the points, lines, etc. are homogeneous, and hence cannot be constructed in the same way as the integers. Nevertheless, in addition to the axiomatic approach to geometry as given by Pasch, Hilbert, Veblen, and others, we still have the expedient of a reduction to the real number system, through the methods of analytic geometry.

However, it is in *set theory* that the axiomatic method plays its most decisive role, since set theory represents the most general and fundamental branch of mathematics and endeavors to lay the foundations for such primary concepts as number, correspondence, function, order, etc. According to Cantor's program, set theory should achieve a genuine "fusion between arithmetic and geometry"; in fact, set theory embraces both the discrete methods of arithmetic and the continuous procedures of analysis and geometry. Because of the failure of the genetic method in set theory, as shown by the paradoxes arising from Cantor's definition of set, the axiomatic method is more important in set theory than in any of the other branches of mathematics.

In 1908 Zermelo gave an axiomatic foundation for set theory distinguished by its simplicity and lucidity; one of his axioms is the axiom of choice. In this paper [Zermelo (1908)] a considerable portion of historical set theory, in particular the theory of equivalence, is derived from the axioms. In the 1920's the axiom of *Aussonderung* (singling out, of subsets), which is most important within Zermelo's system (cf. p. 54), was given a more precise formulation, and another essential axiom, the axiom of substitution, was added. The theory of ordered and well-ordered sets was also developed from these axioms.[14] In accordance with the general axiomatic method, the concept of "set" is not defined; all objects of the axiomatic domain are sets (at least in the later formulations of the theory), "set" being the only primary concept. There is also only one primary (undefined) relation $\in$ ($x \in y$, read "x is an element of y"). Equality is either defined by this membership relation $\in$ or presupposed as a logical concept. The number of axioms, in any formulation of the system, does not exceed nine.

The many merits of this axiomatic foundation of set theory are well recognized, but it does suffer from one weakness, esthetic rather than logical. The formation of sets, which is quasi-constructive[15] apart from the axiom of choice, starts from two sets only, the null set and a certain infinite set which essentially coincides with the set of all positive integers. Due to this strict construction process, there is virtually no fear of paradoxes in the system. On the other hand, and here lies the weakness, the restriction imposed on the domain of set theory by the axioms is rather arbitrary. There is no doubt that no paradoxes would arise even in a far more comprehensive domain.

In the early 1920's John von Neumann[16] proposed an extension of the axiomatic system *just as far as compatible with the exclusion of paradoxes of the types known to us*. The idea is simple and praiseworthy but carries many technical difficulties. The entire plan is based upon the following argument (which is the reason why the axiomatization has been described here in such detail). Actually the "dangerous" sets, such as Ω (the set of all "normal" sets), or Z (the set of all sets), are *not contradictory in themselves*; paradoxes arise only when these sets are allowed *to serve as elements* of themselves or of other sets.

---

[14] Cf. the account in Fraenkel-Bar Hillel (1958), Chapter II, Sections 1–5 and 8. A completely revised edition of this book, with A. Lévy as co-author, will appear in 1966.

[15] Mainly because of the construction of subsets by comprehension; see the end of the present section.

[16] It will be sufficient to refer to von Neumann (1925). In the original form his papers are difficult to understand. Fortunately, Bernays in his 1937–54 papers took a direction which reconciled von Neumann's position with that of Zermelo, and at the same time considerably extended von Neumann's achievements in various respects. Bernays' is the most comprehensive axiomatization of set theory in existence. To a certain extent it was simplified by Gödel (1940), while several papers and books of W. V. Quine and his pupils take directions which, though different, are related to Bernays' ideas; see Quine (1963). [Recently Bernays profoundly modified his views; see Bernays (1958).]

Thus one must distinguish between two different categories of "sets": sets which may also serve as elements of sets, and sets which must not, since otherwise paradoxes would emerge. Surprisingly, the "sets" of the second category can be simply characterized as those which are of "equal extent" [meaning the existence of a (nonformal) mapping] to the "universe," i.e., to the set of all sets. In this case we speak of "classes" rather than of "sets," excluding the classes from membership. This confirms an impression which the paradoxes mentioned above are apt to produce at first, namely, that the contradictions originate from the rather boundless extent of the sets in question. The novelty in the attitudes of von Neumann and Bernays, by comparison with those of Zermelo and his successors, is that the boundlessness need not make these sets inadmissible, but only ineligible to serve as elements.

We conclude this section with two remarks which transcend logic and mathematics and touch on arguments of a philosophical nature.

First, almost simultaneously with the *logical* paradoxes mentioned above, paradoxes of a *semantic* nature were discovered. The following example given by Russell is almost trivial. One may characterize a certain integer in many ways. For instance, 6 is the product of the two smallest prime numbers, but 6 is also the smallest perfect number, "perfect" meaning an integer that equals the sum of its divisors (excluding itself): $6 = 1 + 2 + 3$. Now let us characterize every positive integer by means of a minimal number of words in English. Naturally, only finitely many integers can be characterized by means of less than, say, a hundred words, and since there exist infinitely many integers there also exist infinitely many integers that can only be characterized by means of a hundred or more words. Among these integers, as in any set of positive integers, there is a smallest one: *the smallest positive integer that cannot be characterized by means of less than a hundred words*. But the characterization printed here in italics determines the integer in question by means of only sixteen words!

A less simple and more alarming example of this kind, *Richard's paradox*, is obtained as follows. The set of all decimal fractions which are finitely[17] definable is certainly denumerable. For if k denotes the number of all words, say in English, and n denotes a given positive integer, then at most k^n decimals can be defined by means of n words (of course the actual number is

---

[17] The term "finitely" is actually superfluous, for any definition is given in finitely many words. Cf. the following footnote.

far smaller). Hence, if the decimals are arranged according to the number n of words required for their "briefest" definition (where n can assume any positive integral value) we obtain an enumerated set D_0 which contains all "definable" decimals.[18] (The finite number of decimals corresponding to a fixed n may be arranged arbitrarily.)

Now the diagonal method (p. 23) may be applied to the set D_0 to produce a decimal which does not belong to D_0, that is to say, a (uniquely defined) decimal d_0 which is "not definable." However, we have just defined d_0 by a finite procedure!

Clearly paradoxes of these kinds originate not from logical or mathematical shortcomings but from the vague use of the term "definable."[19] It is easy to produce similar paradoxes; in essence the famous paradoxes of Greek antiquity, such as the Liar ("whatever I say is false") and the Crocodile Argument belong to the same category. These contradictions are produced by faulty *semantics* and not by faulty logic; a more precise foundation for semantics will solve them, and great progress in this direction has recently been made.

Secondly and finally, the complex of problems treated in the present section is to some extent connected with assumptions of a general philosophical nature which nowadays is known as *Platonism*. To describe a typical case let us recall Russell's vicious circle principle (p. 48). Certainly it is logically impossible to construct a certain element of a set S by a definition which refers to S itself. This impossibility appears in various mathematical instances, and we now give three typical different examples.

1. The so-called "fundamental theorem of algebra," stating that any algebraic equation $f(x) = 0$ of positive degree has roots, is sometimes proved

---

[18] Sometimes the objection is made that a single definition may characterize infinitely many concepts (decimals); for instance, all *periodic* decimals. This objection is untenable; for then a *set* has been defined, namely the set of all periodic decimals, and not one or several single decimals.

[19] In the present case, the apparent contradiction between Cantor's proof of the nondenumerability of the continuum (i.e., of the totality of all decimals) and Richard's paradox can be cleared up as follows. Cantor conlusively proves the nonexistence of a mapping between the set of all integers and the set of all decimals. In Richard's argument, there first appears the set of all "definable" decimals and its mapping onto the set of all integers. Yet this very mapping enables us to introduce new decimals, definable in terms of this mapping itself, and by adding the new decimals to those defined already, we obtain a new enumeration (mapping) which allows us to define a third kind of decimals, etc. Richard's method shows that this process of obtaining ever new decimals can be continued without limit, while Cantor's proof shows that no continuation whatsoever will produce *all* decimals.

by the following method, first invented by French mathematicians. A root x is constructed as a complex number for which the absolute value of $f(x)$ for *all* complex x (in a certain domain) is a minimum. Yet this minimum is itself a value of $f(x)$, i.e., a member of the set S of all the values of $f(x)$!

2. On p. 51 we mentioned the axiom of subsets. It yields a subset of a given set S by means of a property (which is meaningful for all elements of S) as follows: the subset contains just those elements of S which have the property in question. For instance, let S be the set of all positive integers, and let the property be "... is a prime number." This method of constructing subsets is sometimes called *comprehension*. Now the question arises whether this method is still admissible if the property is formulated in terms of the *set of all subsets of S*, i.e., the power-set of S. Then a particular subset would be determined by means of the totality of subsets!

3. On p. 46 we introduced the set Ω of Russell's paradox. We discussed there the possibility that Ω might contain itself as an element, in which case Ω would turn out to be a totality which includes among its elements the totality itself. The same applies, even more emphatically, to the set of all sets (p. 47).

Our examples are fundamentally distinct. In the first, as pointed out by Poincaré, instead of referring to *all* the values of $f(x)$ for constructing a minimum, one can refer only to the values of $f(x)$ for rational x and replace the minimum by the lower bound. True, it may happen that the lower bound is also the minimum, hence one of the values $f(x)$; but this is just a coincidence, and is not presumed in the definition.

In the second example, where subsets are defined by comprehension, we may possibly, instead of demanding a "construction", be satisfied with a (unique) "characterization" of the required object (subset). Our attitude then is that mathematicians do not *invent* (construct) their objects but just *discover* them within a pre-existent universe of concepts; in short, our attitude is that of *Platonic realism* (cf. above, p. 54). Then the difficulty disappears, not only in 1 but also in 2, for the number or subset in question is, within the universe of complex numbers or of subsets of a given set, characterized by a certain condition—provided the condition is satisfied by a single number or subset only. The situation obtains in both examples.

In the third example, however, the condition cannot be satisfied at all, because this would imply a contradiction, as we saw earlier. Therefore, as long as we insist that any set can also serve as an element of other sets, full Platonism appears to be refuted by *logical* arguments—a strange situation from a general philosophical point of view. There seems to remain only the alternative of excluding the paradoxes by means of *ad hoc* prohibitions.

So far as restrictions on the universality of membership are concerned, we refer to the remarks on p. 52. Recently a middle course has been proposed which, while excluding over-comprehensive sets such as Ω, constitutes a sort of moderate Platonism.[20] This course still leans on the thesis that mathematical (concepts and) statements possess a reality which is independent of the constructions of the mathematician who (defines and) proves them. The concept of prime number, for instance, or the commutative law $m+n=n+m$ for integers m, n, or the Pythagorean theorem as implied by the axioms of Euclidean geometry, should be meaningful and valid "in any world" and not only for human beings.

The middle course in question must satisfy the requirements of classical mathematics in general. It is based on the *quasi-combinatorial process* (Bernays), the name and nature of which may be explained by the following example. If T is a finite set, for instance the set of integers $\{1, 2, 3, \cdots, 99, 100\}$, then we can characterize any subset of T as an "insertion" of the values "yes" and "no" into T, namely, by attaching "yes" to the elements of T which do belong to the subset and "no" to those which do not.[21] This implies that the above set, like any set of a hundred elements, has just 2^{100} subsets, for one can arbitrarily relate one of the values (yes, no) to each element of the set, independently of the others.

The procedure of insertion can be applied to infinite sets without any change. Thus we find that the set C of all subsets of a denumerable set T—for instance, of the set of the positive integers—has for its cardinal the power $2^{\aleph_0}$ (cf. below p. 63). It is easy to see (cf. above p. 20) that C essentially constitutes, or is equivalent to, the continuum, because real numbers may be represented as sequences (or denumerable sets) of rationals or integers.

---

[20] Cf. Bernays (1935), McNaughton (1957).

[21] The subsets of any finite or infinite set can be characterized in this way. The process of assigning one of two arbitrary values to the elements of sets has far-reaching significance; one then speaks of "charactereristic functions," according to de la Vallée Poussin.

In the above case of a finite set T, we have carried out a "combinatorial" procedure. The assumption that such arbitrary simultaneous choices of a single element out of a pair, say out of the pair (yes, no), are admissible (and thus determine the corresponding subset) even in the case of infinite sets, is the reason for the term "quasi-combinatorial." But this assumption has a platonistic character, since presumably not every subset that is admissible in the quasi-combinatorial sense can be *constructed*, in the sense of comprehension, in terms of a meaningful and "predicative" property (which, for instance, excludes any reference to the set of *all* subsets). In the simplest case of a denumerable set T, the quasi-combinatorial procedure yields the continuum, while no method of constructing the continuum is known.

This quasi-combinatorial procedure and Platonism have a philosophic (epistemologic) nature, and mathematicians will not be prepared to base their theories on philosophy; not even when they personally believe in the epistemologic assumptions and rely on them for the noncontradictory nature of a theory (this nature being largely unprovable). In fact, Bernays himself, in his comprehensive foundation of set theory (Bernays 1937–54), makes no use of the quasi-combinatorial procedure. One can precisely express the sense in which the procedure is too far-reaching: since the axiom of choice is independent of the other axioms, there are certain subsets (cf. p. 35) which cannot be constructed by comprehension and are guaranteed only by "choice." Yet the quasi-combinatorial procedure makes no distinction between them and puts the subsets of the latter kind together with those obtained by comprehension.

(To be sure, a similar non-distinctive attitude is taken in von Neumann's axiomatization of set theory. Bernays, who adopted von Neumann's general starting point, was certainly justified in deviating from von Neumann in this respect.)

The author personally would like to express his satisfaction with a development in which important mathematicians and philosophers, including conceptualists, are inclined towards a moderate form of Platonism—in a generation where some people working on the foundations of mathematics advocate a skeptical attitude and recommend a suicidal reduction of classical mathematics as the only way out of the paradoxes and more general difficulties.

Section 6. Operations with Cardinals

In Sections 4 and 5 we dealt mostly with questions of principle and with logico-mathematical problems. However, even from a logical point of view, an adequate appreciation of set theory is not possible unless the proper mathematical problems of this theory are understoood, at least in general terms.

The results that we have already obtained in the theory of cardinals are enough to make a survey possible without the need for much technical apparatus.[1]

The general *addition* of cardinals is obtained by a generalization of the concept of union (p. 6), as follows. To each element of an arbitrary set we assign a cardinal;[2] corresponding to each of these cardinals we choose a "representative," namely an arbitrary set with that cardinal, with the proviso that no two representatives shall contain common elements. Then the cardinal of the union (sum) of all the representatives is defined to be *the sum of the given cardinals.*

It might appear from this definition as if the sum depended on the choice of the representatives. Yet it is not difficult to see, by means of the axiom of choice, that the unions obtained through different representatives are *equivalent* sets, hence that their cardinals are equal. It is remarkable, and it was recognized only long after the definition had been introduced by Cantor, that the axiom of choice is indispensable even for the definition of addition of cardinals.

By its very definition the addition of cardinals is commutative and, as is easily seen, it is also associative.

---

[1] For additional material see Hausdorff (1914–49) and (1927–57), Kamke (1928–50), Bachmann (1955), Sierpiński (1958), Suppes (1960), Fraenkel (1961).

[2] One may ask, why not simply start with "Suppose we are given an arbitrary *set* of cardinals"? The reason is obvious: among the terms of the sum there may be equal, even infinitely many equal cardinals (see examples 4, 5, 6, 8 below), while any two elements of a set are distinct. Example 8 is especially instructive.

57

EXAMPLES

1. By our definition, the addition of finitely many finite nonzero cardinals (i.e., positive integers) coincides with the ordinary addition of integers in arithmetic.

2. $c + 0 = c$ for any cardinal c.

3. $\aleph_0 + n = \aleph_0 + \aleph_0 = \aleph_0$ (n finite) (cf. p. 14).

4. $\aleph_0 + \aleph_0 + \aleph_0 + \cdots$ (sequence of terms $\aleph_0$) $= \aleph_0$ (cf. p. 15).

5. $\aleph + \aleph = \aleph + \aleph_0 = \aleph$.

6. $\aleph + \aleph + \aleph + \cdots$ (sequence) $= \aleph$.

7. $1 + 2 + 3 + 4 + \cdots = \aleph_0$.

8. If S is the set of all real numbers, let the cardinal $\aleph$ be assigned to each integer of S, $\aleph_0$ to each nonintegral rational, and 1 to each irrational number. The sum of all these cardinals is $\aleph$.

The results 5–8 are obtained as follows. By the remark on p. 20, $\aleph$ may be thought of as the cardinal of an arbitrary segment, say from 0 to 1, or as the cardinal of the double segment or as the cardinal of a "half-line," say from 0 to infinity; here "segment" and "line" are understood to mean the sets of all the points contained in them. This gives 5, 6 and 8. To obtain 7, we may take the following representatives of the integers 1, 2, 3, $\cdots$, respectively,

$$\{a_1\}, \{a_2, a_3\}, \{a_4, a_5, a_6\}, \cdots ;$$

the union of these sets is the denumerable set $\{a_1, a_2, a_3, \cdots, a_k, \cdots\}$. This example shows the *proper addition of infinitely many numbers*, as opposed to the improper addition (by means of the limit-concept) in the theory of infinite series and in the calculus.

To define the *multiplication* of cardinals we use the concept of Cartesian product (p. 35); the product of two (three) cardinals is then the cardinal of the corresponding set of pairs (triplets) etc. Thus, the product of an infinite sequence of cardinals, such as $2 \cdot 2 \cdot 2 \cdot \cdots$, is defined as the cardinal of a set whose elements are infinite sequences, and the elements of these sequences are taken from representatives of the factors (in this case, from pairs). (It is convenient, though not necessary as was the case for addition, to choose representatives without common elements.) Using the axiom of choice we can show that the product of given cardinals is independent of the choice of the representatives (sets) of the given factors (cardinals).

Thus we find that $\aleph_0 \cdot 2 = \aleph_0$, for instance by taking the set of positive integers as the representative of the factor $\aleph_0$ and an arbitrary pair $\{a, b\}$ as the representative of the factor 2. The Cartesian product then contains all pairs

$$\{1, a\}, \{1, b\}, \{2, a\}, \{2, b\}, \{3, a\}, \cdots$$

and is therefore denumerable. Similarly we obtain $\aleph_0 \cdot n = \aleph_0$ for any finite $n \neq 0$, and even $\aleph_0 \cdot \aleph_0 = \aleph_0$.

It is more convenient to obtain the above equalities, and others such as $\aleph \cdot n = \aleph \cdot \aleph_0 = \aleph$, from the examples of addition given on p. 59. To do this we use the following theorem which, in the case of positive integers k_1 and k_2, is well known from arithmetic: the product $k_1 \cdot k_2$ can be obtained by repeated addition of one factor, say k_1, the number of repetitions being given by the other factor k_2. It is easy to show that this theorem is also valid for transfinite factors k_1 and/or k_2.[3] Thus we obtain

$$\aleph_0 \cdot 3 = \aleph_0 + \aleph_0 + \aleph_0 = \aleph_0, \quad \aleph_0 \cdot \aleph_0 = \aleph_0 + \aleph_0 + \aleph_0 + \cdots = \aleph_0.$$

In elementary arithmetic, multiplication is usually *defined* in this way, as repeated addition. In our case this method would be impracticable, or at least very complicated: for in our products the number of the (finite or transfinite) factors may be infinite, and therefore we would be involved in an infinite chain of overlapping additions.

It is not difficult to see that the multiplication of cardinals is commutative and associative. Multiplication and addition are connected by the distributive law. In arithmetic (where only finitely many numbers are added) this law is $a(b + c) = ab + ac$. In fact, distributivity follows immediately from the fact that we can regard multiplication as repeated addition.

Furthermore, by the argument on p. 35, we have:

A product of cardinals is zero if and only if at least one of the factors is zero.

This theorem apparently coincides with the corresponding theorem in arithmetic. However, its origin is quite different. The "if" part of the theorem is trivial here, since it follows from the definition of the Cartesian product (while in arithmetic the "if" part follows from the distributive law). The

---

[3] Since, clearly, $1 \cdot k_2 = k_2$ for every k_2, we infer from the theorem that any cardinal $\neq 0$ can be represented as a finite or infinite sum in which each term is 1.

"only if" part is based on the axiom of choice or, strictly speaking, coincides with this axiom (while in arithmetic the "only if" part follows from the possibility of division).

We now add a more profound example of multiplication to the elementary examples given above. This example is remarkable both for its dramatic history and for its deep influence on the concept, and the problems, of *dimension* (which does not belong to abstract set theory).

On pp. 20–25 we considered $\aleph$ to be the cardinal of the set C whose elements c are all points of the *unit segment*, that is, $0 \leqq c \leqq 1$. On the other hand, every point P of the *unit square* (see Figure 3) is biuniquely determined by its coordinates x, y, hence by the ordered pair (x, y) where $0 \leqq x \leqq 1$, $0 \leqq y \leqq 1$. Therefore one may regard the set of all points in the unit-square as the Cartesian product of C by C,[4] and the cardinal of the set is $\aleph \cdot \aleph = \aleph^2$.

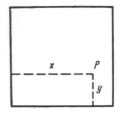

Figure 3

The history of the evaluation of $\aleph^2$ is dramatic. After having proved the existence of the two different cardinals $\aleph_0$ and $\aleph$ in 1873 (p. 20), Cantor was looking for further transfinite cardinals and thought it obvious that he would attain his aim by passing from the one-dimensional continuum ($\aleph$) to continua of higher dimensions. The first step would be to pass from a segment with cardinal $\aleph$ to a square with cardinal $\aleph^2$. Thus he needed a proof that the sets of points contained in a segment and in a square are not equivalent. When he encountered difficulties in searching for this proof he consulted several mathematicians in Berlin and Göttingen. They answered that no proof is required, for it is self-evident that pairs of coordinates (x, y) cannot be reduced, or biuniquely assigned, to a single coordinate! (Much later, in the preface to his excellent book of 1914, Hausdorff called set theory "a field where nothing is self-evident, where true statements are often paradoxical and plausible ones false.") Even in the 1870's Cantor did not rely on the common sense of his famous colleagues and finally, to his

---

4 It does not matter if the factors of the Cartesian product are not disjoint, or even if they are equal, as in this case. The formal difficulty which then seems to arise from the definition of product is easily overcome, either by use of *ordered pairs* instead of plain $\leqq 1$, or by use of another suitable unit-square, for instance the square defined by $0 \leqq x$ pairs, $2 \leqq y \leqq 3$; then the factors of the Cartesian product are disjoint.

great surprise,[5] he found that just the opposite of his conjecture was true, namely, that

The segment and the square are equivalent sets of points.

The gist of the proof is very simple. If the coordinates of an arbitrary point (x, y) of the unit square are written as infinite decimals as on p. 20,

$$x = 0.x_1x_2x_3\cdots, \qquad y = 0.y_1y_2y_3\cdots,$$

they uniquely determine the point of the unit segment

$$z = 0.x_1y_1x_2y_2x_3y_3\cdots .$$

Conversely, an arbitrary point

$$z = 0.z_1z_2z_3z_4z_5z_6\cdots$$

of the segment uniquely yields two coordinates

$$x = 0.\,z_1z_3z_5\cdots, \qquad y = 0.\,z_2z_4z_6\cdots,$$

which determine the point (x, y) of the unit square. By assuming that x and y are *infinite* decimals we have excluded $x = 0, y = 0$; that is to say, we have considered the square without its left and lower side. Similarly, the segment lacks one end-point, $z = 0$.

However, this simple argument requires a slight modification without which we would not obtain a *one-to-one* correspondence between the values z and the ordered pairs (x, y). Though z is an infinite decimal, there are certain exceptional values of z for which our procedure yields finite decimals for either x or y; for instance, $z = 0.11020301020301\cdots$ gives $x = 0.1$, and $z = 0.11203010203010\cdots$ gives $y = 0.1$.

This gap in the proof can easily be filled. One possibility is to use expansions into continued fractions instead of decimal fractions; this method was used by Cantor in 1877 [see Cantor (1932), pp. 119–133]. Still more simply, we can consider not single digits, but groups of digits such that only the last digit of a group differs from 0; then, for instance, $z = 0.5\ 3\ 07\ 009\ 01\ 06\cdots$ gives $x = 0.50701\cdots$, $y = 0.300906\cdots$. Experienced readers will observe

---

[5] He wrote to his friend Dedekind *"je le vois, mais je ne le crois pas"*; see Fraenkel (1930), p. 237].

that this modification is of no importance in principle, since the set of exceptional values itself has only the cardinal $\aleph$.

Cantor's proof yielded the equalities $\aleph^2 = \aleph$, $\aleph^3 = \aleph^2 \cdot \aleph = \aleph$, etc., which show that cardinals greater than $\aleph$ cannot be obtained by passing from one-dimensional to multidimensional continua. Yet, in addition, the proof had a rather shocking effect. It showed that there existed mappings between continua of different dimensions and thus it appeared as if the very concept of *dimension* had become insignificant. Dedekind was the first to point out that Cantor's result does not impair the significance of dimensionality since the concept of dimension depends on the *continuity* of mappings, while any mapping between continua of different dimensions is necessarily discontinuous. Thus Cantor's result started the researches on dimensionality, beginning with Lüroth's proofs that no continuous mapping exists between 1-, 2-, or 3-dimensional continua.[6] The corresponding proof for *any* two different finite dimensions, transcending three-dimensional space, is very difficult; it was first given by Brouwer in 1911.

Finally, we must introduce the *power* a^b into cardinal arithmetic where transfinite cardinals may be used for the base a and the exponent b. We shall not develop the general theory of powers and its applications here. The formal laws for finite powers can be proved to be universally valid. The most important ones are $a^b \cdot a^c = a^{b+c}$ and its generalization to infinitely many factors.

For the applications the most important case is that of the base $a = 2$; for this case we can informally refer the reader to the remarks on pp. 55–56. Thus the set that contains as its elements all the subsets of a (finite or infinite) set B of the cardinal b, has the cardinal 2^b (meaning a product $2 \cdot 2 \cdot 2 \cdots$ with b factors 2). Therefore this set of subsets is called the *power set of B*. By means of the diagonal procedure we proved Cantor's theorem that the power set of B has a greater cardinal than B, i.e., $2^b > b$ for any cardinal b. If B is a denumerable set then the power set is, essentially, the continuum and has the cardinal $2^{\aleph_0} = \aleph > \aleph_0$. These inequalities lead to the continuum problem discussed on p. 44, which asks whether 2^b is *next* to b for every transfinite b.

---

6 Peano (in 1890) constructed a "curve", i.e., a continuous one-dimensional manifold, which passes through every point of a square. Yet this correspondence, while being unique and continuous, is not biunique: there are points of the square through which the curve passes several times.

As remarked above, the arithmetic of cardinals has the same formal laws of *equality* as ordinary arithmetic, viz., the commutative, associative, and distributive laws. (In the following section we shall see that this does not apply to the arithmetic of ordinal numbers.) However, the situation so far as *inequalities* are concerned is rather different. For instance, ordinary arithmetic has the law of "monotonicity": $b < c$ implies $a + b < a + c$. This and other similar laws become invalid for transfinite cardinals. For example, we found (p. 59) that $\aleph + \aleph = \aleph + \aleph_0 = \aleph$, and similarly we have that $\aleph + n = \aleph$ for finite n. These relations express the fact that from the inequalities $n < \aleph_0 < \aleph$ one obtains equalities, and not inequalities, by adding $\aleph$. The same applies to the equalities

$$\aleph_0 + 0 = \aleph_0 + n = \aleph_0 + \aleph_0 \, (= \aleph_0) \qquad (n \text{ finite}, \neq 0)$$

in spite of $0 < n < \aleph_0$. Hence addition, and similarly multiplication, is not generally invertible, i.e., subtraction and division cannot be defined; for instance, $\aleph - \aleph$ and $\aleph/\aleph$ would assume infinitely many different values.

Yet there exist certain rather strange inequalities which are valid for transfinite cardinals; their proofs are mostly difficult and interested readers are referred to the books cited on p. 58.

While on the topic of inequalities we touch a central problem, namely the *comparability of cardinals*. (A full solution of this problem is possible only by methods which depend on the concepts developed in the following Section.) If S and T are sets then, according to the logical principle of the excluded middle, S is either equivalent to at least one subset of T, or S is not equivalent to any subset of T, and the corresponding alternative holds in the direction from T to S. Thus we obtain an exhaustive "disjunction" of cases according to the following scheme.

	S equivalent to a subset of T	S equivalent to no subset of T
T equivalent to a subset of S	First case	Second case: $\overline{\overline{T}} < \overline{\overline{S}}$
T equivalent to no subset of S	Third case: $\overline{\overline{S}} < \overline{\overline{T}}$	Fourth case

According to the definition on p. 41, in the second case the cardinal of T is smaller than that of S, and in the third case the cardinal of S is smaller than that of T. Furthermore, the first case is settled by the

EQUIVALENCE THEOREM. *If each of two sets is equivalent to a subset of the other, then the sets are equivalent. Hence, if S is equivalent to a subset of T, the cardinal of S is either equal to, or smaller than, the cardinal of T, i.e., we have* $\overline{\overline{S}} \leqq \overline{\overline{T}}$.

The second statement follows immediately from the first, by virtue of the above scheme.

We shall give a proof of this theorem, which is far from being trivial though its statement seems obvious. The theorem is fundamental in the theory of equivalence and had been conjectured by Cantor at an early stage; however, he was not able to prove it. The first two proofs were given at the end of the 19th century by F. Bernstein and by Dedekind (the latter proof in a letter to Cantor, published only in 1932). These proofs are based on completely different methods, and the (more than a dozen) proofs published since belong essentially to one or the other of these two categories. The chief difference is that Bernstein, whose proof we shall follow in the main, uses the sequence of the positive integers, essentially in the form of the equality $\aleph_0 + 1 = \aleph_0$, while Dedekind's proof, which was independently rediscovered by Peano and Zermelo in 1906–08, is not based on particular sets and instead rests upon an extremely abstract and powerful procedure. Since that time the theorem has been widely generalized in various directions.

Besides its fundamental significance in the theory of equivalence, the equivalence theorem also has important applications. One of these is the proof of the equivalence of sets between which it is difficult to construct a direct mapping. For instance, by means of the theorem it is easily shown that the set of all *continuous* functions $f(x)$ is equivalent to the continuum (while the set of *all* functions $f(x)$ has a higher cardinal, namely $2^\aleph$).

Proof of the Equivalence Theorem. Let each of the sets S, T be equivalent to a subset of the other, that is to say $S \sim T_1 \subset T$, $T \sim S_1 \subset S$. Our task is to prove that $S \sim T$.

First we express our assumptions in an apparently simpler form. Any mapping between the equivalent sets T and S_1 also maps each proper subset T_1 of T onto a certain subset S_2 of S_1, i.e., $T_1 \sim S_2$; S_2 is obviously a proper subset of S. On the other hand, since the equivalence relation is transitive (p. 8), $S \sim T_1$ and $T_1 \sim S_2$ imply $S \sim S_2$. Finally, in view of $T \sim S_1$, our assertion $S \sim T$ may be written in the form $S \sim S_1$. Hence the equivalence theorem maintains: *If S is equivalent to a proper subset S_2 of itself, then S is* *equivalent to any set* S_1 *"between"* S *and* S_2, i.e., to any subset of S that includes S_2 as a proper subset.

To simplify the notation we shall write A for S_2, B for $S_1 - S_2$ (i.e., for the set of those elements of S_1 which do not belong to S_2), and C for $S - S_1$. Hence we have

$$S_1 = A \cup B, \qquad S = A \cup B \cup C,$$

where the sets A, B, C are mutually disjoint. Then the equivalence theorem states: the hypothesis $A \cup B \cup C \sim A$ implies $A \cup B \cup C \sim A \cup B$. However obvious this statement may appear, any proof of it is far from trivial.

Let ψ be an arbitrary mapping between the sets $A \cup B \cup C$ and A which, by hypothesis, are equivalent. ψ will remain fixed throughout the proof. By applying ψ separately to the complementary subsets A, B, C of $A \cup B \cup C$ we obtain equivalent sets A_1, B_1, C_1, respectively, which are mutually disjoint and complementary subsets of A; in symbols

$$A \sim A_1, \qquad B \sim B_1, \qquad C \sim C_1, \qquad A_1 \cup B_1 \cup C_1 = A.$$

This is the first step of the proof. The second is based upon a mapping ψ_1 between the equivalent sets A and A_1; incidentally, ψ_1 can clearly be taken to be a part of the mapping ψ (and the same applies to the following mappings which yield A_3, A_4, etc.). Because of the relation $A = A_1 \cup B_1 \cup C_1$, ψ_1 yields mutually disjoint subsets A_2, B_2, C_2 of A_1 which satisfy the relations

$$A_1 \sim A_2, \qquad B_1 \sim B_2, \qquad C_1 \sim C_2, \qquad A_2 \cup B_2 \cup C_2 = A_1.$$

This second step is followed by analogous third, fourth, etc, steps. In fact, for every positive integer k we can carry out the kth step, since the successive subsets $A_1, A_2, \cdots, A_k, \cdots$ of A, although decreasing, have the same cardinal, as we see from the relations

$$A \sim A_1 \sim A_2 \sim \cdots \sim A_k \sim \cdots .$$

We also observe the analogous relations

$$(1) \qquad\qquad C \sim C_1 \sim C_2 \sim \cdots \sim C_k \sim \cdots .$$

Now one of two cases will arise. Either *all* the sets A_k ($k = 1, 2, 3, \cdots$) have common elements, in which case the set of these common elements (i.e., the intersection of all the sets A_k) will be denoted by D, or else there are no elements common to all the A_k[7] and the intersection D is the null set. In either case the original set $A \cup B \cup C$ can be represented as the union of the denumerably many (and mutually disjoint) sets D, B, C, B_k, C_k ($k = 1, 2, 3, \cdots$); similarly, the set $A \cup B$ can be represented by omission of the term C. This statement may be illustrated by Figure 4. (If the intersection D differs from the null set, then D corresponds to the congruent rectangles on the left-hand side of the figure.)

---

[7] This case may seem paradoxical since the cardinals of $A, A_1, A_2, \cdots$ do not decrease. Yet this does not exclude the second case, as shown by simple instances such as

$$A = \{0, 1, 2, \cdots\}, A_1 = \{1, 2, 3, \cdots\}, A_2 = \{2, 3, 4, \cdots\}, \cdots, A_k = \{k, k+1, k+2, \cdots\}.$$

Every A_k is infinite (denumerable) and a proper subset of A_{k-1}, but the intersection of all the A_k is empty, because for every positive integer n there are sets A_k which do not contain n, namely A_{n+1} and all subsequent sets.

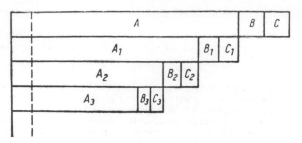

Figure 4

To obtain the desired mapping of $A \cup B \cup C$ onto $A \cup B$, we first split each of these sets into complementary and mutually disjoint subsets as follows.

$$A \cup B \cup C : D, B, C, \ B_1, C_1, B_2, C_2, \cdots, B_k, C_k, \cdots$$
$$A \cup B : D, B, C_1, B_1, C_2, B_2, C_3, \cdots, B_k, C_{k+1}, \cdots .$$

Each subset in the first line will be mapped onto the corresponding subset written beneath it. For the sets D, B, B_k these mappings are trivial, namely the "identical mappings"; that is to say, each element will be assigned to itself. We also have mappings of C onto C_1 and of C_k onto C_{k+1} ($k = 1, 2, 3, \cdots$) at our disposal, in view of the relations (1). Since any element of $A \cup B \cup C$ belongs to one and only one of the sets, the equivalence $A \cup B \cup C \sim A \cup B$ has been shown to be true, and the proof is complete.

Let us repeat that this and similar proofs of the equivalence theorem are based upon the property of the set N of positive integers, that the omission of one of its elements yields a set equivalent to N; in other words, that $\aleph_0 + 1 = \aleph_0$ (p. 59). This makes it possible to omit the set C as we have done above.

As far as the scheme on p. 65 is concerned, there remains only the fourth case. If the reader tries to investigate this case, he will find it rather puzzling. It is only by means of the methods developed in the next section that we shall be able to prove that this case is *impossible*, as Cantor had assumed at an early stage but had not succeeded in proving. Without this proof we cannot assert that *any two sets are comparable* in respect to their cardinals, i.e., that for any cardinals c_1, c_2 we necessarily have one of the cases.

$$c_1 = c_2, \qquad c_1 < c_2, \qquad c_2 < c_1.$$

To fill this gap in the arithmetic of cardinals we must transcend this arithmetic, either explicitly or implicitly.

Section 7. Order, Order Types, Ordinal Numbers.
The Problem of Well-Ordering

Only a superficial survey of the most important problems and results in this field can be given here. However, a few matters of principle will be treated in detail.

It is well known that *order*, in its general logico-mathematical sense, can be introduced as follows. A set (group, field, etc.) S is *ordered* if, in addition to a relation of equality $=$ (which may coincide with identity), a relation $\prec$ that satisfies the following three conditions is defined in S:

a) for any different elements s_1, s_2 of $S(s_1 \neq s_2)$, at least one of the statements $s_1 \prec s_2$ ("s_1 *precedes* s_2"), $s_2 \prec s_1$ holds true;

b) if $s_1 \prec s_2$ then $s_1 \neq s_2$;

c) $s_1 \prec s_2$ and $s_2 \prec s_3$ imply $s_1 \prec s_3$ (*transitivity* of the order relation).

Sometimes one requires that $s_1 \prec s_2$, $s_1 = s_1'$, $s_2 = s_2'$ together imply $s_1' \prec s_2'$. Yet this belongs to the general properties of equality rather than to those of order.

Synonymously with $s_1 \prec s_2$, we write $s_2 \succ s_1$ (" s_2 *follows* s_1").

In view of $s_1 = s_1$, it follows from b) that $s_1 \prec s_1$ is never true (*irreflexivity* of the order relation). Similarly, it follows from b) and c) that $s_1 \prec s_2$ and $s_2 \prec s_1$ are incompatible (*asymmetry* of the relation). Hence, in view of a), we find that one and only one of the statements

$$s_1 = s_2, \qquad s_1 \prec s_2, \qquad s_2 \prec s_1$$

holds true of any two members s_1, s_2 of an ordered set.

From this general notion of order we obtain particular relations by various specializations. As an example we mention the ordering of numbers according to magnitude, as known from ordinary arithmetic. In this case the laws of monotonicity are satisfied for addition and multiplication (p. 64),

67

as well as the Archimedean law[1] which states roughly that one positive number cannot be infinitesimal (infinitely small), or infinitely large, by comparison with another.

In most branches of mathematics, the order relation(s) can be reduced, by suitable definitions, to the primitive relations of the branch in question. In arithmetic, for instance, after the concept of "positive number" has been introduced, the ordering according to magnitude (smaller than) can be defined as follows: a is smaller than b if and only if there is a positive c such that $a + c = b$. Though in set theory one usually introduces order as a primitive (undefined) relation, it is worth asking whether order in sets can be reduced to the general primitive relation of set theory, viz. to the membership relation $\in$.

The answer is in the affirmative, and there are even essentially different ways of attaining this end, among which the simplest is the following. Given a plain (unordered) set S, we introduce an "ordering" set O_S, the elements of which are certain *ordered pairs*[2] (s_1, s_2) of elements of S, provided that O_S satisfies definite conditions which correspond to the conditions a) – c) specified above. (Thus, the conditions demand that $s_1 \neq s_2$, that (s_1, s_2) and (s_2, s_1) shall not both belong to O_S, that whenever (s_1, s_2) and (s_2, s_3) belong to O_S so does (s_1, s_3), and that, for any distinct elements s_1, s_2 of S, either (s_1, s_2) or (s_2, s_1) belongs to O_S. The fulfillment of the second condition follows from that of the first and the third.) Then O_S defines a certain order in S in the usual sense, for instance, if we interpret $s_1 \prec s_2$ as "the pair (s_1, s_2) belongs to O_S."

Recently, *partially ordered sets* have become increasingly important, in addition to the (totally) ordered sets defined above. They are obtained by omitting condition a). We shall confine ourselves to totally ordered sets.

Once the notion of order has been reduced to the set concept, the question of whether *every set can be ordered* assumes a precise meaning, without the apparent vagueness inherent in "can." The question means whether [in view of the general rules (axioms) of set formation] every set S *possesses* at least

---

[1] From the historical point of view one should speak of the law of Eudoxos (who preceded Archimedes by more than a century). But the "Archimedean" terminology, including "non-Archimedean" systems, has spread so widely that it can no longer be eradicated.

[2] Of course, the notion of ordered *pair* is incomparably simpler than the general notion of ordered *set*. Incidentally, ordered pairs can be reduced to plain sets (pairs) by defining the ordered pair (s_1, s_2) as the set $\{\{s_1\}, \{s_1, s_2\}\}$.

one ordering set O_S. The answer is rather surprising. For any S we can construct the set **S** whose elements are *all* ordering sets O_S; yet it cannot be proved without the axiom of choice that in general **S** differs from the null set, i.e., that there always exists at least one ordering set. (If **S** differs from the null set then it is easy to see that for an *infinite* S there are infinitely many different orders. On the other hand, a *finite* set can always be ordered by an elementary method which does not depend on the axiom of choice, namely, by mathematical induction.)

The existence of **S** will not be proved here. The proof involves certain technical, though no fundamental, difficulties.

We shall explicitly clarify the connection between the problem of ordering and the axiom of choice at the end of this section. The reason for postponing it is that, even with the axiom of choice, we do not have any method of proving the existence of a general ordering. We shall establish the existence of a particular ordering (well-ordering, see pp. 75 and 84) which includes ordering but gives more than we require.

We begin the theory of ordered sets with concepts and arguments which parallel the first steps in the theory of equivalence, i.e., of plain sets. The ordered set Q is called *similar* to the ordered set R — in symbols, $Q \simeq R$ — if there is a mapping of Q onto R which *preserves the order*. In other words, if q_1, q_2 are any distinct elements of Q, and r_1, r_2, respectively, are the elements of R assigned to them by the mapping, then $q_1 \prec q_2$ must imply $r_1 \prec r_2$. Every such mapping is called a *similar mapping*. As in the theory of equivalence we see at once that similarity is a reflexive, symmetrical, and transitive[3] relation. We may therefore express $Q \simeq R$ by saying that "Q and R are similar (ordered) sets."

By our definition, the set of all positive integers and the set of all even positive integers are similar if in both cases the integers are ordered by magnitude. In this case there exists only one similar mapping, viz., the one which assigns n to $2n$. Yet, by ordering the positive integers, first in the order of increasing and then in the order of decreasing magnitudes, we obtain different ordered sets N_1 and N_2 which are not similar, though they contain the same elements (and hence would be equal if they were regarded as plain sets). In fact, N_1 has a first (1) and no last element, N_2 has no first but a

---

[3] In distinction to similarity in real life. A child may be similar to both his father and his mother without father and mother being similar to one another.

last element (1), while, for similar sets, clearly either both have a first (last) element, or neither has. The example of N_1 and N_2 shows that we must regard two ordered sets as *equal* only if, in addition to their containing the same elements, these appear in the same order in both sets.

From similarity we proceed to the concept of *order type* (for brevity, *type*) in the same way as we proceeded from equivalence to the concept of cardinal number in Section 2. Hence we shall not here repeat the earlier argument at length. We content ourselves with stating that *similar (ordered) sets, and only such sets, have the same order type*. Following Cantor (cf. p. 9) we denote the type of the ordered set S by $\bar{S}$, because here we have made a single abstraction—disregarding the nature of the elements but not their order. If S is an infinite set then $\bar{S}$ is called a *transfinite type*.

For *finite sets*, cardinal number and order type coincide, in practice if not conceptually. However the arrangement of its elements may be altered, a finite ordered set is transformed into another ordered set which is similar to the original one. Until a century ago this statement was assumed to be empirical, and certainly children are familiar with it from experience in play. Actually, it is a mathematical theorem which can be proved by induction. Because of this result we may use the same symbols $0, 1, 2, 3, \cdots$ for finite cardinals as for finite types (hence for ordinals, see Example 1 below, p. 75). This is also the reason why the same root is used in many languages for cardinal and ordinal numbers, except for the (two) smallest number(s).

For *infinite sets*, however, a change in the order of the elements "in general" also means a change in the order type. A very simple example was given above (N_1 and N_2). In fact, one can show that to a denumerable plain set (of cardinal $\aleph_0$) there correspond $2^{\aleph_0} = \aleph$ ordered sets with the same elements but of different types; in short, there are $\aleph$ different types corresponding to the cardinal $\aleph_0$. The type of an *enumerated* set, for instance of the set of positive integers arranged according to increasing magnitude, is denoted by ω. In general, order types are denoted by small Greek letters.

In contrast with cardinals (see the beginning of Section 5), order types cannot, in general, be arranged "according to magnitude." However, one can define their addition, and to some extent also their multiplication, in a way roughly similar to the definitions for cardinals (Section 6). *Addition* can be defined even as generally as at the beginning of 6, provided the terms (types) in the sum correspond to the elements of an *ordered* set. The result of this addition is called an "ordered sum."

Except in the trivial case of adding finitely many finite types, which coincides with ordinary addition in arithmetic, the commutative law is invalid for the addition of types in general. The simplest counter-example is given by the terms ω and 1. If they are given in the order $(\omega, 1)$ we have to take as representatives an enumerated set whose elements are *followed* by a single (different) element, i.e., by the elements of a unit set, for instance,[4]

$$(1, 2, 3, 4, \cdots) + (0) = (1, 2, 3, 4, \cdots 0).$$

By definition, this ordered set (which has a last element) has the type $\omega + 1$. However, $1 + \omega$ is the type of, say, the ordered set

$$(0) + (1, 2, 3, 4, \quad) = (0, 1, 2, 3, 4, \cdots),$$

which has no last element and is enumerated, i.e., is of the type ω; hence

$$1 + \omega = \omega \neq \omega + 1.$$

In the course of his early work Cantor had been attacked by the argument that his addition of types was absurd because addition ought always to be commutative. He justly retorted that we must not impose our prejudices or expectations on new concepts. After enlarging the domain of integers to such an enormous extent as we did in the theory of transfinite cardinals and types, we should not expect the new numbers to obey the same laws that govern ordinary arithmetic. It is even rather surprising that the addition and multiplication of transfinite *cardinals* conform so widely to the arithmetic of integers, as we saw in Section 6.

In contrast to the situation which obtained when we defined the multiplication of cardinals, we cannot even reasonably *define* the operation of *multiplication* of types in such a way as to include the general case, where infinitely many factors occur. For finitely many factors, we may regard multiplication as repeated addition. In the simplest case of two factors, the second will be considered to be the multiplier and the first the

---

4 To avoid confusion between plain sets and ordered sets when denoted by (the totality of) their elements, we shall put the elements in *round* parentheses in the case of an ordered set; the order inside the parentheses then suggests the order defined in the set. For the sake of generality, we shall do so even for unit sets, for which the notion of order is trivial.

multiplicand, and this definition can be extended to any finite number of factors either by induction or directly. Even for two factors α, β we must in general distinguish between the products $\alpha \cdot \beta$ and $\beta \cdot \alpha$. The product $\alpha \cdot \beta$ means a sum in which the term α occurs "as often and in the order" defined by β. Hence, for instance, $2 \cdot \omega = 2 + 2 + 2 + \cdots = \omega$, while $\omega \cdot 2 = \omega + \omega$ clearly differs from ω. Cf. Examples 4 and 5 below.

We shall not dwell further on types in general but shall concentrate on the most important types, the ordinals. However, it should be pointed out here that, by using the order types, Cantor and his successors succeeded in solving problems which had been attacked without avail for many centuries. The problem that is most interesting from both the philosophical and the mathematical points of view is that of the linear *continuum*; that is, the problem of completely characterizing the set of all points on a line, or of all real numbers, as a (linear) ordered abstract set. Some Greek philosophers and, later, Thomas Aquinas and other scholastics, had dealt with the continuum, starting from various (and partly opposed) assumptions. Like many later philosophers they reached no conclusive results. They interpreted their failure by regarding the continuum either as a religious (rather than a logico-mathematical) concept or as an intuitive primary concept not capable of further logical analysis. By general concepts in his theory of ordered sets, Cantor succeeded[5] in characterizing the order type of the linear continuum by relatively simple properties which are purely ordinal (not metrical).

We now turn to the last theme of this booklet. It is, among all the subject matter of set theory, the one most suitable for applications and the one most used in other branches of mathematics: the well-ordered sets and the ordinals.

DEFINITION I. An ordered set, every nonempty subset of which has a *first* element, is called *well-ordered*. The order type of an (infinite) well-ordered set is called a (transfinite) ordinal number or, for brevity, an *ordinal*.

Thus, any well-ordered set itself has a first member, and each of its subsets, as well as any set similar to a well-ordered set, is also well-ordered. For practical reasons the null set and every unit set are also considered to be well-ordered.

---

5 See Cantor (1932), pp. 310f.

We use the term "ordinal *number*," in contrast to "order *type*," in view of the simple properties of these particular types (in particular Theorem 5 on p. 79). These properties distinguish them not only from types in general but even from cardinal numbers, so far as we have explored them. In fact they are the most natural generalization of the positive integers.

There are other equivalent characterizations of the concept of a well-ordered set. We advise the readers to prove that, for instance, each of the following definitions is fully equivalent to Definition I:

a) An ordered set W is well-ordered if, for every subset of W which is followed by some elements in W, there exists in W an element *immediately* following the subset. (This implies in particular that any element of W that is not the last element of W has an immediate successor in W; furthermore, by taking the subset to be the null set, we see that W contains a first element.)

b) An ordered set is well-ordered if it contains no infinite sequence of elements a_k with the property

$$\cdots \prec a_{k+1} \prec a_k \prec \cdots \prec a_3 \prec a_2 \prec a_1.$$

At the beginning of the present section we mentioned a method of reducing the order relation to the membership relation, i.e., of reducing ordered sets to plain sets. Such a reduction is also possible for the concept of a well-ordered set, without the full detour involved in having to consider order in general.

EXAMPLES OF WELL-ORDERED SETS

1) Any finite ordered set is well-ordered. Hence all finite types 0, 1, 2, 3, $\cdots$ are ordinals.

2) The infinite ordered set $(0, 1, 2, 3, \cdots)$ is of type ω, hence ω is an ordinal.

3) The set $(a_0, a_1, a_2, \cdots b_0, b_1, \cdots, b_{k-1})$ has the type (ordinal) $\omega + k$.

4) The set $(1,5,9,\cdots 2,6,10,\cdots 3,7,11,\cdots 4,8,12,\cdots)$ has the type (ordinal) $\omega + \omega + \omega + \omega = \omega \cdot 4$.

5) The set

$(1,2,3,5,7,11,\cdots$ [all prime numbers]; $4,6,9,10,\cdots$; $8,12,18,20,\cdots$; $16, \cdots \cdots)$

contains the positive integers ordered according to the number of their (distinct or equal) prime factors, while the integers with the same number of prime factors are arranged in order of magnitude. This ordered set has the type (ordinal)

$$\omega + \omega + \omega + \cdots = \omega \cdot \omega.$$

This is easy to see, since the subset consisting of all the integers which precede 2^k has the type $\omega \cdot (k-1)$, provided $k > 1$.

On the other hand, the set of *all* integers ordered according to magnitude (so that, for instance, $-5 \prec -2 \prec 3$) is not well-ordered, nor is the set of positive integers in the arrangement

$$(1,3,5,7,\cdots \cdots,8,6,4,2).$$

In the first case, the set itself, has no first element; in the second, the subset of all even numbers has no first element.

We shall formulate here, because of their outstanding importance, a few of the theorems that apply to well-ordered sets and ordinal numbers. (*In what follows, "set" will always mean "well-ordered set."*) Some of these theorems involve the notion of section, which belongs to the general theory of ordered sets. We introduce it by

DEFINITION II: The set of all elements of an ordered set W which precede a certain element a of W is called a *section* of W; more precisely, the section *determined by* a.

Clearly, any section of W is a proper subset of W. In particular, if W has a first element (as any *well*-ordered W has) then the null set is the section determined by the first member.

THEOREM 1. *The union (ordered sum) of finitely many mutually disjoint well-ordered sets is well-ordered no matter in what order the terms are taken; hence the sum of finitely many ordinals is always an ordinal. The same applies to infinitely many terms, provided their arrangement corresponds to a well-ordered set.*

Cf. Examples 3–5 above.

THEOREM 2. *A set cannot be similar to a section of itself.*

It is easy to check this in the case of Examples 2–4 above.

DEFINITION III. If S and T are sets of the types (ordinals) σ and τ, respectively, and if S is similar to a section of T, then σ is called *smaller than* τ ($\sigma < \tau$). Synonymously with $\sigma < \tau$, we write $\tau > \sigma$ ("τ is *greater than* σ"). (As for types in general, the equality of ordinals $\sigma = \tau$ is defined by the similarity of corresponding sets.)

It is essentially Theorem 2 which enables us to define this order between ordinals "according to magnitude," for by Theorem 2 the order relation so defined is irreflexive, that is, $\sigma < \sigma$ is not true for any σ. Then it is easy to see that the order relation is also asymmetrical (and, of course, transitive); cf. p. 69. However, we cannot immediately conclude from the definition that the relation is also connective, i.e., that of any two different ordinals one is smaller than the other. This property is contained in the more profound Theorem 5.

THEOREM 3. *A set which is well-ordered both in the given arrangement of its members and in the reverse arrangement* (*obtained by replacing every $a \prec b$ with $b \prec a$*) *must be finite.*

In other words, an infinite ordered set is either not well-ordered itself, or else the set obtained by inversion of its order relations is not well-ordered. (Naturally, it may be that both sets are not well-ordered; for instance, the set of all rational numbers ordered according to magnitude.) Thus, by use of the concept of well-ordering, we have an entirely new definition of finiteness, applying to both sets and numbers (cf. the beginning of Section 4).

THEOREM 4. *The set of all ordinals that are smaller than a given ordinal σ, can be ordered according to increasing magnitudes of the ordinals; the ordered set $W(\sigma)$ obtained in this way is well-ordered, and the type of $W(\sigma)$ is just the ordinal σ* (*which is the immediate successor of the elements of $W(\sigma)$*). *In symbols,*

$$\overline{W(\sigma)} = \sigma.$$

Before giving a proof of this fundamental and nonelementary theorem, we shall illustrate it by a few examples.

a) $\sigma = 0$. Since no ordinal is smaller than 0, $W(0)$ is the empty set $\emptyset$, the ordinal of which is indeed 0.

b) $\sigma = 3$. By Definition III, the ordinals smaller than 3 are 0,1,2, and this is their order by magnitude. In fact, the ordered set (0,1,2) has the type 3. This example shows, as do all others for finite σ, the importance of listing 0 among the ordinals (and cardinals), and so of including the null set among the sets; Cantor regarded 1 as the smallest (cardinal and) ordinal.

c) $\sigma = \omega$. As is easily seen, an ordinal is smaller than ω if and only if it is finite. Hence

$$W(\omega) = (0,1,2,3,\cdots),$$

and this set has the type ω.

d) $\sigma = \omega + 1$. By Definition III, the only transfinite ordinal which is smaller than $\omega + 1$ is ω, for if S is a set of the type $\omega + 1$, ω is the type of section of S which is determined by the *last* member of S. Hence

$$W(\omega + 1) = (0,1,2,3,\cdots, \omega),$$

and this set has the type $\omega + 1$.

Proof of Theorem 4. Let S be an arbitrary well-ordered set and σ its type (ordinal). Since any element μ of $W(\sigma)$ is an ordinal $< \sigma$, it follows from Definition III that S has a section (obviously unique), whose type is μ. Hence if μ_1 and μ_2 are different elements of $W(\sigma)$, they are the types of different sections of S determined by elements s_1 and s_2 of S respectively. Depending on whether $s_1 \prec s_2$ or $s_2 \prec s_1$ in S, we have $\mu_1 < \mu_2$ or $\mu_2 < \mu_1$. (This result, reached without comparability, is due to the assumption that both μ_1 and μ_2 are smaller than the same ordinal σ.) As is easily seen, $W(\sigma)$ is an ordered set in the sense given at the beginning of the present section (including transitivity).

But $W(\sigma)$ is even *well*-ordered, as we shall show by constructing a similar mapping of $W(\sigma)$ onto the well-ordered set S. If μ is an element of $W(\sigma)$ (i.e., $\mu < \sigma$) then let μ be assigned to the element s of S that determines in S the section of type μ (see above). Clearly, this rule defines a one-to-one correspondence between the elements of $W(\sigma)$ and those of S. Moreover, the mapping constructed in this way is *similar*. To see this we consider different elements s_1, s_2 of S and the corresponding ordinals μ_1, μ_2 belonging to $W(\sigma)$; if $s_1 \prec s_2$ in S then $\mu_1 < \mu_2$, hence $\mu_1 \prec \mu_2$ in $W(\sigma)$. Finally, in view of the similarity, the ordinal σ of S is also the ordinal of $W(\sigma)$ as stated in our theorem. The proof of the theorem is thus complete.

In view of Theorem 4, $W(\sigma)$ may be regarded as the *standard set* of the ordinal σ. This will be used in the following proof of the central theorem of the theory of well-ordered sets, namely,

THEOREM 5 (Comparability of Well-Ordered Sets with Respect to their Ordinals). *Two well-ordered sets are either similar to one another, or one is similar to a section of the other. Hence one and only one of the relations*

$$\sigma = \tau, \qquad \sigma < \tau, \qquad \tau < \sigma \quad (\text{i.e.,} \quad \sigma > \tau)$$

holds between two ordinals σ, τ.

Proof. Our procedure is analogous to that on p. 65, where the problem was the comparability of *plain sets* with respect to their *cardinals*. There we did not complete the proof because we were not able to deal with the fourth case, while here Theorem 4 enables us to exclude the fourth case.

If S and T are sets of ordinal σ and τ respectively, we shall replace them by the similar standard sets $W(\sigma)$ and $W(\tau)$ respectively, whose elements are ordinals. Let I be the intersection of $W(\sigma)$ and $W(\tau)$; as a subset of well-ordered sets, I itself is well-ordered. According to the definition of W in Theorem 4, if a fixed ordinal belongs to I, then so does every smaller ordinal. I then "begins" with $0, 1, 2, \cdots$. If I does not coincide with $W(\sigma)$, I is obviously a section of $W(\sigma)$, and a corresponding alternative holds for I and $W(\tau)$. Thus we obtain the following scheme, which is analogous to the scheme at the end of Section 6.

	$I = W(\sigma)$	I section of $W(\sigma)$
$I = W(\tau)$	First case: $W(\sigma) = W(\tau)$	Second case: $W(\tau)$ section of $W(\sigma)$
I section of $W(\tau)$	Third case: $W(\sigma)$ section of $W(\tau)$	Fourth case

In the first case, since $S \simeq W(\sigma)$ and $T \simeq W(\tau)$, we have $S \simeq T$, that is, $\sigma = \tau$. Similarly, in the second case T is similar to a section of S, and in the third, S is similar to a section of T, that is, $\tau < \sigma$ or $\sigma < \tau$ respectively, according to Definition III.

Finally, *the fourth case is impossible*. It would mean, according to our scheme, that the ordinal (type) of I was smaller than both σ and τ. Hence, if μ denotes the ordinal which immediately follows all the ordinals contained in I [cf. a) on p. 75], μ must belong to both sets $W(\sigma)$ and $W(\tau)$, and so also to their intersection I, whereas any element of $I = W(\mu)$ is an ordinal *smaller* than μ. This contradiction shows that only the previous three cases can occur, which concludes the proof of Theorem 5.

Having dealt so far with the ordinals (types) of well-ordered sets, we infer from Theorem 5 a far-reaching result about their cardinals, namely,

THEOREM 6 (Comparability of Well-Ordered Sets with Respect to their Cardinals). *The cardinals of two well-ordered sets are either equal, or one cardinal is smaller than the other.*

This is an immediate consequence of Theorem 5, in view of the equivalence theorem (see p. 65). If we denote the well-ordered sets by S and T respectively, then according to Theorem 5, the first case means $S \simeq T$. Therefore $S \sim T$ in view of the definition of similarity; but $S \sim T$ expresses the fact that the cardinals of S and T are *equal*.

The alternative, by Theorem 5, is that one of the sets is similar to a section of the other. Now, a section is a proper subset; hence S is *equivalent* to a subset of T, or T is *equivalent* to a subset of S, or both. By the equivalence theorem this means that the cardinal of S equals, or is smaller than, the cardinal of T, or that the cardinal of T equals, or is smaller than, the cardinal of S. Checking all three cases we find that the cardinal of S is equal to, or is smaller or greater than, the cardinal of T, which is just the assertion of Theorem 6.

If we distinguish between these cases, we find that

$$S < T \quad \text{implies} \quad \overline{\overline{S}} \leqq \overline{\overline{T}} \quad \text{and} \quad T < S \quad \text{implies} \quad \overline{\overline{T}} \leqq \overline{\overline{S}},$$

whereas

$$S = T \quad \text{implies} \quad \overline{\overline{S}} = \overline{\overline{T}}.$$

Thus the comparability of cardinals, which could not be proved in the preceding section for cardinals of plain sets, has been shown to hold for *well-ordered* sets.

In addition to comparability there is another property which well-ordered sets share with finite sets and numbers, namely inductivity; that is, the possibility of giving proofs and definitions by induction. This property has many fundamental applications; it is a natural generalization of the process of "mathematical" induction in arithmetic and is here called "transfinite" induction. "Mathematical" (or, as it is called in continental languages, "complete") induction is, of course, meant as an antithesis not to transfinite induction but to the incomplete induction used in natural sciences.

THEOREM 7 (Proof by Transfinite Induction). *Let $\mathfrak{P}(x)$ be a property or statement that is meaningful for all elements x of a given well-ordered set W. If*

a) *$\mathfrak{P}$ is true for the first element of W, and*
b) *the truth of $\mathfrak{P}$ for all the elements of W which precede a certain element x, implies its truth for x,*

then $\mathfrak{P}$ is true for all elements of W.

Proof. Let us assume that this is not the case, i.e., that the subset of W which contains those x for which $\mathfrak{P}$ is *not* true, is not empty. Since W is well-ordered, the subset has a *first* member x_0, which by a) is certainly not the first member of W. By the definition of x_0, $\mathfrak{P}$ is true for all elements of W which precede x_0; therefore, by b), $\mathfrak{P}$ must be true for x_0 also. This contradiction shows that our assumption is untenable, which completes the proof.

Theorem 7 justifies the use of transfinite induction in *proofs*. Much more profound and just as useful for applications is the use of transfinite induction in *definitions*; a simple example is the definition of powers α^β by transfinite induction (see below). It was only in 1923 that J. von Neumann discovered that definitions by transfinite induction, which had been used for a long time, need justification, which is not at all simple. The situation is similar in many respects, though not all, to that of mathematical induction in arithmetic: although it had been used in proofs for many centuries, its use in definitions (for instance, in defining the addition and multiplication of integers) was justified for the first time by Dedekind in 1888, and in another way (independently) in the 1920's.

In Theorem 4 we started with an ordinal σ and stated that the ordered set of all ordinals smaller than σ is well-ordered and has exactly the ordinal σ. It is not difficult to invert this statement, with the following result. A set of ordinals which, whenever it contains an ordinal, also contains every smaller ordinal, can be ordered according to the magnitude of its elements and then constitutes a well-ordered set whose ordinal is just the successor of all its elements. We now use this result to exhibit one of the most daring and beautiful of Cantor's inventions, namely the "continuation of the series of positive integers beyond infinity" (cf. p. 3), meaning *the series of all (finite and transfinite) ordinals*.

As remarked above, this series starts with the ordinal 0, which is followed by the other finite ordinals in their usual order; the finite ordinal n is then the type of the well-ordered set of all the smaller ordinals $(0,1,2,\cdots,n-1)$. Similarly the well-ordered set (sequence) of *all finite ordinals* $(0,1,2,\cdots)$ has the (transfinite) ordinal ω, which is the successor of all the finite ordinals. By proceeding to the following ordinals $\omega + 1$, $\omega + 2$, $\cdots, \omega + n, \cdots$, we obtain another sequence which, together with the first, produces a set of the ordinal $\omega + \omega = \omega \cdot 2$. Thus the series of ordinals "begins" as follows:

$$0, 1, \cdots, n, \cdots \omega, \omega + 1, \cdots \omega \cdot 2, \omega \cdot 2 + 1, \cdots \omega \cdot 3, \cdots \omega \cdot m + n, \cdots$$

where m and n denote finite ordinals. The ordinal of the well-ordered set (sequence of sequences) of *all* these ordinals is $\omega \cdot \omega = \omega^2$. Thus its continuation is

$$\cdots \omega^2, \omega^2 + 1, \cdots \omega^2 + \omega \cdot m + n, \cdots \omega^2 \cdot 2, \cdots \omega^2 \cdot k + \omega \cdot m + n, \cdots \omega^3,$$

$$\cdots \omega^n, \cdots \omega^n \cdot k_0 + \omega^{n-1} \cdot k_1 + \cdots + \omega \cdot k_{n-1} + k_n, \cdots$$

The elementary arithmetical operations with ordinals which we introduced above, do not include one which denotes the successor of all these ordinals. However, we can define *powers* α^β of ordinals, for instance by means of transfinite induction, and then it turns out that the well-ordered set of all ordinals introduced so far has precisely the ordinal ω^ω; this, then, is the desired successor.

Hence we obtain a continuation of the series of ordinals in the form

$$\omega^\omega, \omega^{\omega+1}, \cdots \omega^\omega \cdot 2, \cdots \omega^\omega \cdot \omega, \cdots \omega^\omega \cdot \omega^\omega = \omega^{\omega \cdot 2}, \cdots \omega^{\omega^2}, \cdots \omega^{\omega^3}, \cdots \omega^{\omega^n}, \cdots$$

The successor of all these ordinals is ω^{ω^ω}, i.e., the ω^ωth power of ω. One can proceed further and reach the ordinals

$$\omega^\omega, \cdots \omega^{\omega^\omega}, \cdots \omega^{\omega^{\omega^\omega}}, \cdots .$$

However, the successor of all these, written $\omega^{\omega^{\omega^{\cdots}}}$ by means of a sequence of powers, cannot be expressed in finite form by means of our operations. This successor is denoted by ε_0 and constitutes the smallest *epsilon-number* if, following Cantor's terminology, we refer to any ordinal ε which satisfies the relation $\omega^\varepsilon = \varepsilon$ as an epsilon-number.

Contrary to expectation,[6] all these ordinals are "relatively small," namely the types of *denumerable* well-ordered sets; hence the corresponding cardinal is the smallest transfinite cardinal $\aleph_0$. We now prove this for the ordinal ω^ω by actually arranging all the positive integers according to the type ω^ω, which differs from their arrangement according to the type ω^2 (see p. 76, Example 5) as follows:

1, 2, 3, 5, 7, 11, $\cdots$ (all prime numbers);
4, 6, 10, 14, $\cdots$; 9, 15, 21, $\cdots$; 25, 35, 55, $\cdots$;
8, 12, 20, 28, $\cdots$, 18, 30, 42, $\cdots$; $\cdots$; 27, 45, 63, $\cdots$; $\cdots$; 125, $\cdots$; $\cdots$
16, 24, 40, $\cdots$; 36, $\cdots$; 54, $\cdots$; $\cdots$; 81, $\cdots$

$\cdots$

To make this scheme easier to understand we remark that, apart from the integer 1, the nth line of our arrangement contains the products of n (distinct or equal) prime numbers, ordered in an easily comprehensible way; hence the set containing the integers that precede 2^k has the ordinal ω^{k-1} [while in the example of p. 76 it has only the ordinal $\omega \cdot (k-1)$].

Our arrangement confirms that ω^ω is the ordinal of a denumerable well-ordered set; in short, a *denumerable ordinal*. This can also be inferred from a general theorem, which shows that ε_0 and far greater ordinals are also denumerable. Yet the set of *all denumerable transfinite ordinals* is not denumerable; if its elements are ordered by magnitude, then its type is *the least nondenumerable* ordinal (see p. 82). Following Cantor, this well-ordered set is called the *second number class* (while the first, containing the finite ordinals, has the ordinal ω). The problems of the second number class are still far from being solved; we have become acquainted above with only a minute quantity of its elements, and its full extent seems impossible to comprehend. The second number class is followed by a third,

---

6 Since $\aleph_0$ is the cardinal corresponding to the ordinal ω, one would expect $\aleph_0^{\aleph_0}$ to be the cardinal corresponding to the ordinal ω^ω. This is not true. One easily finds that $\aleph_0^{\aleph_0} \geq 2^{\aleph_0} = \aleph > \aleph_0$ (in fact $\aleph_0^{\aleph_0}$ *equals* $\aleph$ and even $\aleph^{\aleph} = \aleph$). Yet, as will be seen presently, the cardinal corresponding to ω^ω is only $\aleph_0$.

fourth, etc., which are defined similarly. Thus, we obtain well-ordered sets of ever-increasing cardinals, independently of the procedure for obtaining increasing cardinals (of plain sets) by the construction of power sets (Section 5).

Yet when we try to enjoy the "paradise" of Cantor's series of ordinals to its full extent it turns out, unfortunately, that the picture is too good to be true. Let Z^* be the well-ordered set of *all* ordinals, and let φ be the ordinal of Z^*. By Theorem 4, the set of the ordinals *less* than φ has the ordinal φ ; hence this set is similar to, and even coincides with, Z^*. In other words, φ ought to be greater than any ordinal, including φ itself. This contradiction shows that there cannot be *a set containing all ordinals.* Z^* constitutes the earliest paradox of set theory (1897), the *Burali-Forti paradox*, which was also known to Cantor [see Cantor (1932), p. 445]. For its "resolution" cf. the remarks in Section 5.

In the sixth century B.C. it was discovered by the Pythagorean School that there exist "incommensurable" (irrational) numbers such as $\sqrt{2}$. The leaders of the school considered this discovery so revolutionary, and even politically dangerous, that they kept it an esoteric secret. In the two and a half millenia which have since elapsed, hardly any proof of a mathematical theorem has been so strongly disputed and has caused mathematicians and logicians such deep and continuing concern (including Homeric oratory, otherwise very unusual in the mathematical world) as *Zermelo's first proof of the well-ordering theorem* [Zermelo (1904)]; cf. p. 36. Even today the discussions centered around this theorem have not come to an end. We formulate it as follows:

WELL-ORDERING THEOREM. *Given a (plain or ordered) set S, there exists a well-ordered set W which contains exactly the elements of S. In short, any set can be well-ordered.*

If convenient, one can clearly drop the qualification "exactly." For if W contains additional elements, the subset of W that contains exactly the members of S is also well-ordered, as a subset of a well-ordered set. It would even suffice to have a well-ordered set *equivalent* to S, for any mapping of it onto S produces a well-ordering of S.

We shall give below a proof of the theorem which should not cause any great difficulty to readers acquainted with mathematical methods. It is essentially just Zermelo's first proof; his second proof is more difficult to understand. Yet we precede the proof by some remarks directed to readers in general: remarks about the *meaning* and the *consequences* of the theorem and about the *methods* available for its proof.

The (more usual) second formulation ("can" be well-ordered) is of a subjective nature. Therefore the first formulation is preferable. It reduces the problem to a question about the existence of sets, the examination of which can be objectively based on the axioms of set theory and on the reduction of (well-)ordering to the membership relation (see the beginning of Section 7). Thus the well-ordering theorem asserts that, because of the axioms, for any S there exists a well-ordering of S. It should be noted, however, that this is a nonconstructive, purely existential statement.

A decisive role is played in the proof of this statement by the axiom of choice (Section 4), which transmits its existential nature to the proof of our theorem. The axiom of choice would hardly have provoked so much opposition had it not been for its connection with, and even equivalence to, the well-ordering theorem. In fact, nobody took offense so long as only arithmetical operations (notably addition and multiplication of cardinals, see Section 6) were attained by means of the axiom (even without an explicit statement of it). However, when the axiom was used by Zermelo to prove our theorem, which had been asserted by Cantor long before without a shadow of proof, the axiom was attacked by many leading mathematicians. The resistance to the axiom arose not because they found fault with its statement but because they refused to accept such a far-reaching consequence as the well-ordering theorem. Since most of these skeptics could not discover a fault in the proof itself, they attacked the basis of the proof, namely the axiom of choice. This skeptical attitude was heightened by the fact that the proof contains no constructive element that might contribute to actually well-ordering the given set S; hence it is not surprising that our theorem is of no avail for solving the continuum problem (p. 37). Actually, as soon as one acknowledges the existential nature of the theorem, these facts should not arouse alarm.

In 1908 Zermelo gave a second proof of the well-ordering theorem. The use of the axiom of choice is identical (and inevitable) in both proofs, but they differ fundamentally in the techniques used. The first proof relies on essentially *mathematical* methods and results, notably on the comparability of well-ordered sets (Theorem 5). The second proof operates without properly mathematical tools and instead uses *logical* methods, in particular the "theory of chains" developed by Dedekind in 1888. It is just this abstract nature of the proof that makes it more difficult to understand. [A third proof, which somehow combines the logical advantages of both, is contained in the fourth paper in the sequence of Bernays (1937–54).]

Not only does the axiom of choice form the basis of any proof of the well-ordering theorem, but the axiom can easily be deduced from this theorem, as an hypothesis. In fact, if we assume that theorem, we obtain the axiom in its "multiplicative" form, which starts with a *disjoint* set S of nonempty sets (p. 34). The argument is as follows: Let the union of the elements of S be well-ordered. Hence the subsets of the union, among them the elements of S, are also well-ordered. Then the set that contains just the *first* element of each well-ordered element of S is a choice set of S. In particular, these first elements are distinct from one another since S is disjoint. Hence *the axiom of choice and the well-ordering theorem are equivalent principles*; if one of them is assumed to be true then the other can be proved.

Proof of the well-ordering theorem. Let S be a nonempty (plain or ordered) set. Our aim is to well-order S, that is, to form a well-ordered set which contains exactly the elements of S.

For this purpose we shall use an arbitrary choice function f (p. 33) which will be fixed throughout the proof. Here f assigns a uniquely determined element $f(S_0)$ of S_0 to every nonempty subset S_0 of S; for brevity this will be called "the *distinguished* element of the subset S_0."

Furthermore we define *gamma sets* (of S), an *ad hoc* concept introduced by Zermelo, by the following two properties:

1. any gamma set is a *well-ordered* subset of S, independently of whether S is ordered or not;
2. if Γ is any gamma set of S and A any *section* of Γ determined by the element a of Γ, then

$$a = f(S - A).$$

(We shall disregard the trivial case when Γ is the null set $\emptyset$, in which case both properties are satisfied "vacuously.")

We illustrate the second property, which is not so easily understood at first, by a few examples. If $A = \emptyset$ then $S - A = S$; on the other hand, the element a of any Γ that determines the section $\emptyset$ is the first element of Γ. For $A = \emptyset$, then, the second property expresses the fact that the first element of *any* gamma set is the distinguished element of S itself; we denote it by $c_0 \, (=f(S))$. Thus the unit set (c_0), which is trivially well-ordered, is a gamma set—the simplest such set.

If Γ contains at least two elements (of which the first is certainly c_0), then the second property implies that the second element c_1 of Γ satisfies the relation $c_1 = f(S - (c_0))$; for the section of Γ determined by its second element is the set whose only element is c_0, the first element of Γ. Hence c_1 is the second element of any gamma set.

In the same way, for a sufficiently comprehensive set S we obtain the gamma sets $(c_0, c_1, c_2, \cdots, c_n)$ for arbitary integral n, or even for *all* integral n. Like any finite ordered set, these sets are well-ordered. Their elements are characterized by the property that for $k = 0, 1, 2, \cdots, n$, c_k is the distinguished element of the subset of S obtained by omission of the elements $c_0, c_1, \cdots, c_{k-1}$. Hence c_k proves to be the $(k+1)$-th element of any gamma set; if S is an infinite set we thus obtain infinitely many gamma sets.

As shown by these examples, the connection between any element a of a gamma set Γ and the section A of Γ determined by a is (by the second property) that a is, in view of the fixed choice function f, the distinguished element of $S - A$; i.e., of the subset of S obtained by omitting the elements of A. Thus, the distinguished element a *immediately follows* the elements of the well-ordered section A. If S were already well-ordered (which is our aim), then the choice function would assign its first element a to any nonempty "remainder" $S - A$.

Cantor assumed that by constructing all well-ordered sets $(c_0, c_1, \cdots, c_k, \cdots)$ we would reach the aim of well-ordering S. This assumption is erroneous, for it is far from clear that the process is certain to *exhaust* the given set S. Sometimes it was thought that one might use the series of ordinals for this purpose, letting a sufficiently large number of elements with transfinite indices $c_\omega, c_{\omega+1}, \cdots$ follow the c_n with finite n. But in order to ensure that the process is exhaustive one must use the series of all ordinals, which involves the Burali-Forti paradox (p. 84).

After these preliminary remarks we start with the proof, splitting it up into four steps (of which only the second demands careful attention from the reader).

I. *Of two different gamma sets Γ_1 and Γ_2 of S, one is a section of the other.*

Proof. By Theorem 5 above, at least one set is *similar* to a section of the other, or to the other itself; this follows from the first property of gamma sets. Incidentally, the above examples make our assertion plausible, since they show that any sufficiently comprehensive gamma set starts with the same elements $c_0, c_1, \cdots, c_n, \cdots$. We may assume that $\Gamma_1 \simeq \Gamma_2'$, where Γ_2' is a section of Γ_2, or Γ_2 itself. By transfinite induction we immediately see that the sets Γ_1 and Γ_2' are not only similar but even equal. In fact, their first elements are the same, namely c_0, the distinguished element of S. If there are corresponding elements in Γ_1 and Γ_2' which are distinct, let $c_1{}^*$ be the *first* member of Γ_1 that is assigned to a *different* member $c_2{}^*$ of Γ_2 by the similar mapping[7] of Γ_1 onto Γ_2'. But then, the sections C_1 of Γ_1 and C_2 of Γ_2', determined by $c_1{}^*$ and $c_2{}^*$ respectively, must coincide: $C_1 = C_2$. Hence, by the second property of gamma sets, we obtain

$$c_1{}^* = f(S - C_1) = f(S - C_2) = c_2{}^*,$$

contrary to the assumption $c_1{}^* \neq c_2{}^*$. The contradiction results from the assumption that there are corresponding *different* members in Γ_1 and Γ_2', and so it shows that $\Gamma_1 = \Gamma_2'$. That is, if $\Gamma_1 \neq \Gamma_2$ then Γ_1 is a section of Γ_2. This completes the proof of I.

We have thus seen that, as suggested by the above examples, the "initial" coincidence of any two gamma sets extends throughout the "shorter" set. Therefore, two gamma sets with some common element also coincide in respect to all preceding elements, and if they have two elements in common then their order is the same in both sets.

II. *The totality of members of all gamma sets of S can be well-ordered in such a way that the order relations prevailing in every single gamma set are retained.*

---

[7] It easily follows from Theorem 2 that there exists a unique similar mapping between similar well-ordered sets.

First, the union of all the gamma sets is a plain set that contains all elements of gamma sets. We define an order in the union by the following rule: If s_1 and s_2 are different elements of the union, then let $s_1 \in \Gamma_1$ and $s_2 \in \Gamma_2$. (Of course, Γ_1 and Γ_2 are not determined by s_1 and s_2.) By I, either $\Gamma_1 = \Gamma_2$ or one is a section of the other; hence there are gamma-sets Γ which contain both s_1 and s_2. Then *the order of s_1 and s_2 in the union shall be the same as in Γ.*

This rule seems arbitrary and ambiguous since, in general, there are many sets Γ which contain both s_1 and s_2. But if Γ and Γ' are two gamma sets that contain s_1 and s_2 then, according to the final remark in I, their order in both sets is the same; hence our rule is unambiguous. From the same final remark in I it follows that the order defined by our rule is also transitive. Therefore, the union has been transformed by our rule into an *ordered set* which from now on we shall denote by Σ.

To show that Σ is well-ordered, i.e., that any nonempty subset Σ_0 of Σ has a first element, let s_0 be an arbitrary element of Σ_0 and Γ a gamma set that contains s_0. Then every element of Σ_0 which precedes s_0 is also an element of Γ, and it precedes s_0 in Γ, by the final remark in I (and the order defined in Σ). Hence, if s_0 is not the first element of Σ_0, the section of Σ_0 determined by s_0 is a nonempty subset of Γ, and therefore has a first element; this shows that Σ is well-ordered.

III. *The set Σ is a gamma set; hence (because of its definition) the most comprehensive gamma set of S.*

As proved in II, Σ satisfies the first property of gamma sets. So far as the second property is concerned, let a be an element of Σ and A the section of Σ determined by a. By the definition of Σ, a belongs to a gamma set Γ, and by the end of the proof in II, A is also the section of Γ determined by a. By the second property of Γ we have $a = f(S-A)$. Since a was supposed to be an arbitrary element of Γ, this equality shows that Σ also satisfies the second property. Therefore Σ is a gamma set.

Clearly, the proof of III, and the end of the proof of II, are based on the possibility of identifying Σ, as far as we need to, with a suitable gamma set, which transmits its properties to Σ.

IV. *Σ contains all elements of the given set S.*

We prove this indirectly, by assuming that there is an element of S outside Σ, and by showing that this implies the existence of a gamma set more comprehensive than Σ, contrary to the result III.

If S contained an element not belonging to Σ, the complement $S-\Sigma$ would be nonempty; let $z = f(S-\Sigma)$ be its distinguished element. We define a new well-ordered set $\Sigma^* = \Sigma + (z)$ by adding z, which does not belong to Σ, to the elements of Σ, following all of them. Then Σ^* is a gamma set. To prove the second property of Σ^* we recall that this property was already proved in III for all elements of Σ and for the corresponding sections. All that remains, then, is to examine the last element z of Σ^*. But for z the second property is simply the equality $z = f(S - \Sigma)$, by means of which z was defined above.

Hence Σ^* would be a gamma set more comprehensive than Σ, contrary to the result III. The contradiction shows that $S - \Sigma$ is empty, that is, $\Sigma = S$. Since Σ is well-ordered, we have completed the proof of the well-ordering theorem.

The significance and the consequences of the well-ordering theorem are to a large extent given by Theorems 6 and 7 above. Once any set can be well-ordered — no matter whether or not an actual well-ordering can be specified (the latter applying in the case of the continuum, for instance) — we infer from Theorem 6 that any two (plain) sets are comparable with respect to their cardinals. In other words, for any two cardinals c, d (and not only for cardinals of well-ordered sets) we have the trichotomy

$$c = d \quad \text{or} \quad c < d \quad \text{or} \quad c > d.$$

Thus we have at last solved the problem of comparability, left open in Section 6.

We stressed above that the axiom of choice and the well-ordering theorem are *equivalent* principles. The same can be proved, although in a less elementary way, for the comparability theorem. In other words, not only does comparability follow from well-ordering but, conversely, by assuming comparability, we can prove the well-ordering theorem without using the axiom of choice [see Hartogs (1915)]. Thus choice, well-ordering, and comparability prove to be equivalent; if one of these principles is assumed, the other two follow as logical consequences. For many other equivalents discovered later, see Rubin-Rubin (1963).

Following Cantor, the cardinals of well-ordered sets are called *alephs* and denoted by $\aleph_0, \aleph_1, \aleph_2, \cdots \aleph_\omega, \cdots$ ($\aleph_0$, the least aleph, is already known to us as the cardinal of denumerable sets). One can show that any aleph $\aleph_n$, and even any set of alephs, has an immediate successor in the sense of magnitude. By the well-ordering theorem, the continuum "can" also be well-ordered, hence its cardinal $\aleph$ must be an aleph $> \aleph_0$. The continuum problem (p. 37) may then be formulated as the following question: is $\aleph = \aleph_1$ (the second aleph) or greater than $\aleph_1$ (and, in the latter case, with which aleph does $\aleph$ coincide)?

Finally, in view of Theorem 7, and according to the well-ordering theorem, the powerful instrument of transfinite induction can be applied to any set. This has far-reaching consequences not only in analysis and topology but also, for instance, in algebra. The remark of Steinitz quoted on p. 36 refers to this application of the well-ordering theorem.

Thus it becomes clear in what sense the theory of well-ordered sets and of ordinals may be regarded as the most applicable part of set theory. Yet the decisive instrument for this purpose, the well-ordering theorem, which is based on the axiom of choice, has not only a mathematical nature but also a logical and perhaps even an epistemological nature.

Bibliography

Bibliography

Only those books and papers are mentioned to which reference has been made in the text. Besides the textbooks and treatises on set theory [Bachmann (1955), Fraenkel (1961), Halmos (1960), Hausdorff (1914–49) and (1927–57), Hessenberg (1906), Kamke (1928–50), Klaua (1964), Quine (1963), Sierpiński (1928) and (1958), Suppes (1960)], Cantor's original work [see Cantor (1932)] is still of interest today.

Bachmann, H., 1955. *Transfinite Zahlen* (*Ergebnisse der Math.* etc., N.S., H. 1) Berlin-Göttingen-Heidelberg. 204 pp.

Bar-Hillel, Y.,1952. Bolzano's propositional logic. *Archiv f. Math. Logik u. Grundlagenforschung* 1, 65–98.

See also under *Fraenkel*

Bernays, P., 1935. Sur le platonisme dans les mathématiques. *L'Enseignement Math.* 34, 52–69.

—, 1937-54. A system of axiomatic set theory. I–VII. *Jour. f. Symbolic Logic* 2,6,7 (bis), 8,13,19.

— (and A. A. Fraenkel), 1958. *Axiomatic set theory*. Amsterdam. 226 pp.

See also under *Hilbert*

Bolzano, B., 1851. *Paradoxien des Unendlichen.* (Edited posthumously by *F. Přihonsky*.) *New ed.*, Leipzig, 1920. 157 pp. English ed., 1950. 189pp.

Bridgman, P.W., 1934. A physicist's second reaction to Mengenlehre. *Scripta Math.* 2, 101–117, 224–234.

Brouwer, L. E. J., 1907. *Over de grondslagen der wiskunde.* (Dissertation) Amsterdam and Leipzig. 183 pp.

—, 1912. *Intuitionisme en formalisme.* Groningen. 32 pp. (English translation in *Bull. of the Amer. Math. Soc.* 20 (1914), 81–96.)

Cantor, G., 1932. *Gesammelte Abhandlungen mathematischen und philosophischen Inhalts.* Ed. by *E. Zermelo*. Berlin. 486 pp. Reprinted 1961.

Carnap, R., 1958. *Introduction to symbolic logic and its applications.* New York. 241 pp.

Cohen, Paul J., 1963-64. The independence of the continuum hypothesis. *Proc. of the National Acad. of Sc.* (U.S.A.) 50 (1963), 1143–1148, and 51 (1964), 105–110.

Dedekind, R., 1888. *Was sind und was soll. die Zahlen?* Braunschweig. (6th ed., 1930.) 58 pp. English ed., Chicago and London, 1901.

Fraenkel, A. (A.), 1922. Über den Begriff "definit" und die Unabhängigkeit des Auswahlaxioms. *Sitzungsber. der Preuss. Akad. der Wissensch.*, Phys.-Math. K., 1922, 253–257.

—, 1930. Georg Cantor. *Jahresber. der Deutschen Mathem.-Vereinigung* 39, 189–266. (Also published separately.)

—, 1935a. Sur l'axiome du choix. *L'Enseignement Math.* 34, 32–51.

—, 1935b. Zum Diagonalverfahren Cantors. *Fundamenta Math.* 25, 45–50.

—, 1961. *Abstract set theory.* Amsterdam. (First appeared 1953.) 2nd ed., 295 pp. Revised ed. will appear in 1966.

— and *Y. Bar-Hillel*, 1958. *Foundations of set theory*. Amsterdam. 415 pp. Revised ed. will appear in 1966.

Frege, G., 1884. *Die Grundlagen der Arithmetik*. Breslau. 119 pp. (Reprinted 1934 and 1961.) English ed., 1950.

Gödel, K., 1940. *The consistency of the axiom of choice and of the generalized continuum-hypothesis with the axioms of set theory*. Princeton N. J., 66 pp. Revised ed. 1951, 74 pp.

—, 1947. What is Cantor's continuum problem? *Amer. Math. Monthly* **54**, 515–525.

Gutberlet, C,. 1886. Das Problem des Unendlichen. *Zeitschr. f. Philos. und philos. Kritik*, N.F. **88**, 179–223.

Halmos, P. R., 1960. *Naive set theory*. Princeton N. J. 110 pp.

Hartogs, F., 1915. Über das Problem der Wohlordnung. *Mathem. Annalen* **76**, 438–443.

Hausdorff, F., 1914/49. *Grundzüge der Mengenlehre*. Leipzig, 1914. 476 pp. Reprinted New York, 1949.

—, 1927/57. *Mengenlehre*. Berlin and Leipzig, 1927. 235 pp. English ed., New York, 1957. (2nd ed., 1962, 352 pp.)

Hessenberg, G., 1906. *Grundbegriffe der Mengenlehre*. Göttingen. 220 pp.

Heyting, A., 1956. *Intuitionism—An introduction*. Amsterdam. 133 pp.

Hilbert, D., 1918. Axiomatisches Denken. *Math. Annalen* **78**, 405–419.

—, 1925. Über das Unendliche. *Ibidem* **95**, 161–190.

—, and *P. Bernays*, 1934. *Grundlagen der Mathematik*. I. Berlin. 471 pp. Reprinted Ann Arbor, Mich., 1944.

Kamke, E., 1928–50. *Mengenlehre*. Berlin and Leipzig. 160 pp. (4th ed., 1962, 194 pp.) English ed., New York, 1950. 144 pp.

Klaua, D., 1964. *Allgemeine Mengenlehre*. Berlin (Akademie-Verlag). 581 pp.

Kleene, S.C., and *Vesley, R.E.*, 1964. *The foundations of intuitionistic mathematics*. Amsterdam, 256 pp.

Kreisel, G., 1950. Note on arithmetic models for consistent formulae of the predicate calculus. *Fundamenta Math.* **37**, 265–285.

Lebesgue, H., 1941. Les controverses sur la théorie des ensembles et la question des fondements. *Les Entretiens de Zurich sur les Fondements et la Méthode des Sciences Math. 1938* (Zurich 1941), pp. 109–122.

Lindenbaum, A., and *A. Mostowski*, 1938. Über die Unabhängigkeit des Auswahlaxioms und einiger seiner Folgerungen. *C. R. des Séances de la Soc. des Sciences et des Lettres de Varsovie*, Cl. III, **31**, 27–32.

McNaughton, R. 1957. Conceptual schemes in set theory. *The Philosoph. Review* **66**, 66–80.

Menger, K., 1933. Neuere Methoden und Probleme der Geometrie. *Verhandl. des Internat. Mathem.-Kongresses Zürich 1932*, I (1933), 310–323.

Mirimanoff, D., 1917–20. Les antinomies de Russell et de Burali-Forti et le problème fondamental de la théorie des ensembles etc. *L'Enseignment Mathem.* **19** (1917), 37–52, 209–217; **21** (1920), 29–52.

Mostowski, A., 1939. Über die Unabhängigkeit des Wohlordnungssatzes vom Ordnungsprinzip. *Fundamenta Math.* **32**, 201–252.

See also under *Lindenbaum*.

von Neumann, J., 1925. Eine Axiomatisierung der Mengenlehre. *Jour. f. d. Reine u. Angew. Math.* **154**, 219–240. (Cf. *ibidem* **155**, 128.)

Pasch, M., 1882. *Vorlesungen über neuere Geometrie*. Leipzig. 202 pp. (New ed. with a contribution of *M. Dehn*, Berlin. 1926. 275 pp.)

Peano, G., 1890. Sur une courbe qui remplit toute une aire plane. *Math. Annalen* **36,** 157–160.

Poincaré, H., 1910. *Sechs Vorträge über ausgewählte Gegenstände aus der reinen Mathematik und mathematischen Physik.* Leipzig and Berlin. 60 pp.

Quine, W.V.O., 1963. *Set theory and its logic. Cambridge, Mass.* 359 pp.

Ramsey, F. P., 1926. The foundations of mathematics. *Proceed. of the London Mathem. Soc.* (2) **25,** 338–384.

Rubin H. and *J.E. Rubin*, 1963. *Equivalents of the axiom of choice.* Amsterdam. 158 pp.

Russell, Bertrand, 1903. *The principles of mathematics.* I. London. 2nd ed. with a new introduction, 1937. 534 pp. Reprinted 1950.

—, 1908. Mathematical logic as based on the theory of types. *Amer. Jour. of Math.* **30,** 222–262.

—, 1919. *Introduction to mathematical philosophy.* London and New York. 206 pp. 6th impression, 1948.

See also under *Whitehead.*

Scholz, H., 1931. *Geschichte der Logik.* Berlin. 78 pp. English ed., New York, 1961. 140 pp.

—, and *H. Schweitzer*, 1935. *Die sogenannten Definitionen durch Abstraktion.* Leipzig. 106 pp.

Sierpiński, W., 1928. *Leçons sur les nombres transfinis.* Paris. 240 pp. Reprinted 1950.

—, 1958. *Cardinal and ordinal numbers.* Warszawa. 487 pp.

Steinitz, E., 1910. Algebraische Theorie der Körper. *Jour. f. d. Reine u. Angew. Math.* **137,** 167–309. New ed. by *R. Baer* and *H. Hasse,* Berlin and Leipzig, 1930, 155 pp. +27 pp. notes.

Suppes, P., 1960. *Axiomatic set theory.* Princeton, N. J., 265 pp.

Tarski, A., 1925. Sur les ensembles finis. *Fundamenta Math.* **6,** 45–95.

Weyl, H., 1949. *Philosophy of mathematics and natural science.* (Revised and augmented English ed. of the German ed. published 1926.) Princeton, N. J., 311 pp.

Whitehead, A. N., and *B. Russell*, 1910–13. *Principia Mathematica.* 3 vols. 666+772+491 pp. 2nd ed., with a new Introduction and Appendices, 1925–27.

Zermelo, E., 1904. Beweis, dass jede Menge wohlgeordnet werden kann. *Mathem. Annalen* **59,** 514–516.

—, 1908. Untersuchungen über die Grundlagen der Mengenlehre. I (was not continued). *Ibidem* **65,** 261–281.

Author Index

Subject Index

List of Symbols

Author Index

d'Alembert, J.R. (1717–1783) 1
Archimedes (287–212 B. C.) 70
Aristotle (384–322 B. C.) 2
Augustinus (354–430) 2

Bachmann, H. 40, 58, 92
Bar-Hillel, Y. 2, 39, 48, 51
Belinfante, H.J. (1896–1942) 48
Bernays, P. 30, 51 f., 55–57, 86
Bernstein, F. (1878–1956) 65
du Bois Reymond, P. (1831–1889) 2
Bolzano, B. (1781–1848) 2, 16, 91
Boole, G. (1815–1864) 7
Bridgman, P.W. 22
Brouwer, L.E.J. 48, 63
Burali-Forti, C. (1861–1931) 84, 87

Cantor, G. (1845–1918) *passim*
Carnap, R. 10
Cauchy, A.-L. (1789–1857) 1
Crescas, Hasdai (c. 1340–1412) 2
Cohen, Paul J. 37

van Dantzig, D. (1901–1959) 48
Dedekind, R. (1831–1916) 20, 50, 62–65, 81, 86, 91
Descartes, R. (1596–1650) 2, 9

Euclid (Eukleides) (c. 320. B.C.) 1, 12, 24, 36, 49 f.
Eudoxos (c. 410–c. 355 B.C.) 70

Fourier, J.-B. J. (1768–1830) 90
Fraenkel, A.A. (1891–1965) 2, 22, 39, 48, 51, 58, 62, 92
Frege, G. (1848–1925) 10, 47, 50

Galileo, G. (1564–1642) 16
Gauss, C.F. (1777–1855) 1
Gödel, K. 37, 39, 45, 51
Gutberlet, C. (1837–1928) 2

Halmos, P.R. 92
Hankel, H. (1839–1873) 2

Harnack, A. (1851–1888) 2
Hartogs, F. (1874–1943) 89
Hausdorff, F. (1868–1942) 25, 38, 58, 62, 92
Hessenberg, G. (1874–1925) 42, 92
Heyting, A. 48
Hilbert, D. (1862–1943) 20, 30, 45, 49, 91
Hume, D. (1711–1776) 9

Kamke, E. (1890–1961) 58, 92
Kant, I. (1724–1804) 2
Klaua, D. 47, 92
Kleene, S. C. 48
Kreisel, G. 22

Lebesgue, H. (1875–1941) 38, 90
Leibniz, G.W. (1646–1716) 2, 5, 9
Levi, B. 36
Lévy, A. 51
Lindenbaum, A. (1904–1941) 39
Locke, J. (1632–1704) 2
Lucretius, T.L.C. (98–55 B.C.) 2
Lüroth, L. (1844–1910) 63

McNaughton, R, 55
Menger, K. 90
Méray, H.C. (1835–1911) 1
Mirimanoff, D. (1861–1925) 39
de Morgan, A. (1806–1878)
Mostowski, A. 39

von Neumann, J. (1903–1957) 51 f., 57 f., 81, 91
Newton, I. (1642–1727) 1

Pasch, M. (1843–1930) 9, 50
Peano, G. (1858–1932) 30, 50, 63, 66
Plato (c. 429–c. 348 B.C.) 38, 50
Poincare, H. (1854–1913) 22, 36, 54

Quine, W.V.O. 51, 92

Ramsey, F.P. (1903–1930) 38

Richard, J. 53
Riemann, B. (1826–1866) 12, 90
de Rimini, G. (?–1358) 2
Rubin, H. and J.E. 40, 89
Russell, B. 8, 26, 32, 34f., 38, 46ff.,
    50, 54, 91

Scholz, H. (1884–1956) 2
Schumacher, H.C. (1780–1850) 1
Sierpiński W. 92
Spinoza, B. (1632–1677) 2
Steinitz, E. (1871–1928) 36f., 89
Suppes, P. 58, 92

Tarski, A. 26
Thomas Aquinas (1225–1274) 2
de la Vallée Poussin, C.J. (1866–1962) 55
Veblen, O. (1880–1960) 50
Vesley, 48

Weierstrass, K. (1815–1897) 1
Weyl, H. (1885–1955) 9, 49
Whitehead, A.N. (1861–1947) 10, 38

Zermelo, E. (1871–1956) 33–37, 51 f.,
    66, 84–86, 91
Zorn, M. 40

Subject Index

(Generally the page referred to is the page on which the term is introduced.)

Addition, see sum
Algebraic number, 16
Antinomies, see paradoxes
Archimedean law, 70
Associative, 7; 60
Axiom (principle) of choice, 32–37
Axiomatic method, 49–51

Belongs, 4
Biunique, 7
Boolean algebra, 7

Cantor's theorem, 42
Cardinal (number), finite, transfinite, 9–11
Cartesian product, 35, 59
Choice function, 33
Choice set, 34
Commutative, 7, 60
Comparability, 64f., 79f., 89
Comprehension, 31, 54
Contains, 4
Continuum, 19, 25, 61, 74
Conbinuum problem, hypothesis, 37, 44, 89

Definition by abstraction, 9f.
Denumerable, 13
Diagonal (method, process), 21, 23, 43
Different, 5
Dimension, 63
Disjoint, 6, 34
Distributive, 7, 60

Element, 4
Enumerated, 14
Equal (ordered sets), 72
Equal (sets), 5
Equivalence theorem, 65
Equivalent, 8

Greater than, 41, 77

Includes, 5
Induction, inductive, 26, 28, 81
Intersection, 6
(Neo-) intuitionism, 48

Mapping, 7
Mapping, similar, 71
Member, 4

Membership relation, 51
Multiplication, see product

Null set, 4
Number class, 83

One-to-one correspondence, 7
Order, ordered set, 69
Ordinal (number), finite, transfinite, 7

Paradox of Burali-Forti, 84
Paradox of Richard, 53
Paradox of Russell, 46f
Platonism, 51 ff.
Power set, 42
Powers of cardinals, 63
Powers of ordinals, 82
Predicate, property, 8
Product of cardinals, 59
Product of order types, 74

Rational (number), 14
Real number, 20
Reflexive, 8, 28
Relation, 8

Section, 76
Sequence, 6
Set, 4
Set, finite, 26, 29, 77
Set, infinite, 26, 28
Similar, 71
Smaller than, 41, 77
Subset (proper), 5
Sum of cardinals, 58
Sum order-types, 73
Symmetrical, 8

Tertium non datur, 46
Theory of types, 47
Transcendental number, 24
Transitive, 8
(Order) type, finite, transfinite, 72

Union, 6
Unit set, 42

Vicious circle principle, 48

Well-ordered set, 75
Well-ordering theorem, 84

101

List of Symbols

$\emptyset$	4	$\subseteq$	5
$\aleph_0, \aleph$ etc.	25, 89	$\sim$	8
ω	72	$\simeq$	71
$\{\ \}$	5	$+$	6, 59
$(\ )$	6	$-$	13
$\bar{S}$	72	$\cdot$	59
$\bar{\bar{S}}$	9	$<, >$	41, 77
$=$	5	$\prec, \succ$	69
$\neq$	5	$\cup, \cap$	7
$\subset$	5	$\in$	51

ABCDE69876